K¹² Math⁺

All photographs are royalty-free. © Artville

About K12 Inc.
K12 Inc., a technology-based education company, is the nation's leading provider of proprietary curriculum and online education programs to students in grades K–12. K^{12} provides its curriculum and academic services to online schools, traditional classrooms, blended school programs, and directly to families. K12 Inc. also operates the K^{12} International Academy, an accredited, diploma-granting online private school serving students worldwide. K^{12}'s mission is to provide any child the curriculum and tools to maximize success in life, regardless of geographic, financial, or demographic circumstances. K12 Inc. is accredited by CITA. More information can be found at www.K12.com.

ISBN: 978-1-60153-079-0
Printed by RR Donnelley, Roanoke, VA, USA, May 2015

Contents

iv

Addition Facts with Sums Through 12

Addition Facts with Sums Through 20

Addition Strategies

Introduction to Subtraction

Subtraction Facts Through 20

Subtraction Strategies

Place Value, Addition, and Subtraction

Add or Subtract: Problem Solving

Add or Subtract: More Problem Solving

Geometric Figures, Data, and Attributes

Semester Review and Checkpoint

Printouts

Addition Facts Chart
Five-in-a-Row Grid Paper
Horizontal Picture Graph
Hundred Chart
Hundred Grid
Inch Grid Paper
Number Line 0–100
Numeral Writing Guide
Paper Clock Model
Part-Part-Total Sheet
Start-Change-Result Chart
Subtraction Facts Chart
Subtraction Strategy Cards
Tally Chart
Ten-Frames
Vertical Picture Graph

Numbers Through 50

Read Numbers

Read the number on each sport jersey.

T R Y   I T

1. Count aloud the numbers in order from 10 to 30.

2. Count aloud the numbers in order from 15 to 28.

3. Count aloud the numbers in order from 1 to 50.

4. Count aloud the number of cats.

5. Which of these numbers is forty-six? Circle the answer.

   A. 64   B. 46   C. 406

6. What number is this?

   13

7. What number is this?

   27

8. What number is this?

   0

Write Numerals Through 50

Fill In the Numbers

Write the missing numbers.

1	2	3	4	___	6	7
8	9	10	11	12	13	___
15	16	17	18	19	___	21
22	___	24	___	26	27	28
___	___	31	___	33	34	35
36	___	___	39	40	___	42
___	44	45	___	47	48	49
___						

TRY IT

1. Write the number eighteen.

2. Write the number forty.

3. Write the number zero.

4. Write the number seventeen.

5. Write the missing number.

8, 9, _____ , 11, 12, 13

TRY IT

Count by 10s and 5s Through 50

More Skip Counting

Count by 5s or 10s to find the missing number.

1. 10, 15, 20, _____ , 30

2. 10, 20, 30, 40, _____

3. 20, 25, 30, _____ , 40

4. 25, 30, 35, 40, _____

Count by 5s or 10s to find the total.

5.

_____ beach balls

6.

_____ blocks

7.
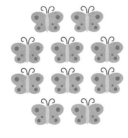 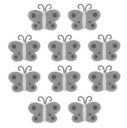 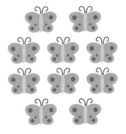 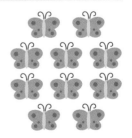

_____ butterflies

TRY IT

Circle the answer.

8. Count by 5s.

Choose the missing number. 15, _____, 25, 30, 35

A. 16   B. 20   C. 40   D. 26

9. Count by 5s.

Choose the missing number. 25, 30, 35, 40, _____

A. 35   B. 20   C. 41   D. 45

10. Count by 10s.

Choose the missing number. 10, _____, 30, 40, 50

A. 25   B. 11   C. 15   D. 20

11. Count by 10s.

Choose the missing number. 10, 20, 30, _____, 50

A. 51   B. 40   C. 31   D. 45

Say the answer.

12. Skip count aloud by 5s from 25 through 50.

13. Skip count aloud by 10s from 30 through 50.

Count by 2s Through 50

Count by 2s

Skip count by 2s to write the missing number.

1. 26, 28, 30, 32, _____

2. 36, 38, _____ , 42, 44

3. 34, _____ , 38, 40, 42

4. _____ , 20, 22, 24, 26

Skip count by 2s to find the total number of objects.

5.

_____ gloves

6.

_____ shoes

7.

_____ eyes

8.

_____ legs

TRY IT

Say the answer.

9. Start at 2 and skip count by 2s to 24.

10. Start at 20 and skip count by 2s to 40.

11. Start at 30 and skip count by 2s to 50.

Skip count by 2s to write the missing numbers.

12. 26, 28, _____, 32, _____, _____, 38

13. 40, 42, _____, 46, 48, _____

14. 12, 14, _____, _____, 20, _____, 24

TRY IT

Numbers Through 100

Count & Read Numbers Through 100

Read each number aloud.

17 20 38 44

50 59 60

77 78 88 89

91 92 100

Count aloud.

1. Count from 38 to 78.

2. Count from 60 to 89.

TRY IT

Read the number aloud.

3. 52

4. 67

5. 83

Count aloud the number of beach balls.

6.

TRY IT

Write Numerals Through 100

Fill In the Hundred Chart

Complete the hundred chart.

1	2	3	4	5	6	7	8	9	10
11	12	13	14	___	16	1_	18	19	20
21	2_	3_	24	25	2_	27	28	___	30
31	32	33	34	35	36	37	38	39	40
41	42	43	44	4_	46	47	48	49	50
___	___	___	___	___		57	58	___	___
6_	62	___	6_	65	66	6_	___	___	70
___	7_	73	___	___	___	___	___	9_	___
___	___	___	___	___	___	___	8_	9_	90
___	2_	93	___	___	___	9_	9_	___	___

TRY IT

Write the number.

1. ninety-eight

2. sixty-eight

3. seventy-three

4. ninety-nine

Write the missing number.

5. 96, 97, 98, 99, _____

6. 50, 51, _____, 53, 54, 55

7. 68, 69, _____, 71, 72

8. 74, 75, _____, 77, 78

TRY IT

Count by 10s and 5s Through 100

Skip Count by 5s and 10s

Count by 10s or 5s to find the missing number.

1. 60, 70, 80, _____, 100

2. 75, 80, 85, 90, _____

3. 60, _____, 70, 75, 80

4. 40, 50, 60, _____, 80

Each cookie has 5 chocolate chips. Each watermelon slice has 10 seeds. Count aloud by 5s or 10s to find the total number of chips and the total number of seeds.

5.

_____ chocolate chips

6.

_____ watermelon seeds

T R Y   I T

Read the problem and follow the directions.

7. Count by 10s. Circle the missing number.
60, 70, 80, 90, _____

A. 100   B. 91   C. 95   D. 75

8. Color the numbers on the chart to show counting by 5s from 55 to 100.

51	52	53	54	55	56	57	58	59	60
61	62	63	64	65	66	67	68	69	70
71	72	73	74	75	76	77	78	79	80
81	82	83	84	85	86	87	88	89	90
91	92	93	94	95	96	97	98	99	100

9. Maro has 9 boxes. Each box has 10 gumdrops. How many gumdrops are there? Circle the answer.

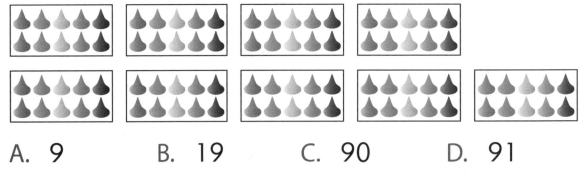

A. 9   B. 19   C. 90   D. 91

10. Count aloud by 10s to 100.

TRY IT

Count by 2s Through 100

Skip Count by 2s

Count by 2s. Write the missing number.

1. 92, 94, 96, 98, _____

2. 76, 78, 80, 82, _____

3. 68, _____, 72, 74, 76

4. 56, 58, 60, _____, 64

5. Use a yellow crayon. Color the numbers that you would say when you skip count by 2s from 72 to 100.

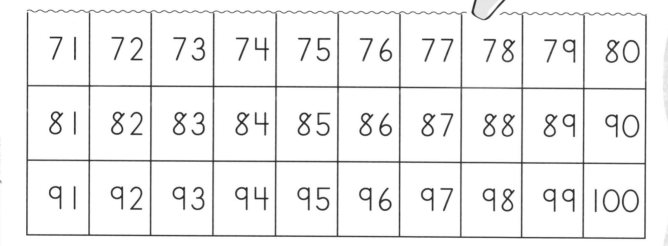

71	72	73	74	75	76	77	78	79	80
81	82	83	84	85	86	87	88	89	90
91	92	93	94	95	96	97	98	99	100

T R Y   I T

Count by 2s. Circle the missing number.

6. 88, 90, 92, _____

    A. 91   B. 95   C. 97   D. 94

7. 50, 52, _____, 56, 58

    A. 51   B. 52   C. 53   D. 54

Count by 2s. Write the missing numbers.

8. 90, _____, 94, _____, _____, 100

9. 78, _____, 82, _____, 86, _____

Say the answer.

10. Start at 60 and skip count aloud by 2s to 80.

11. Start at 80 and skip count aloud by 2s to 100.

TRY IT

Compare Numbers Through 100

Show How Numbers Compare

Circle the greater number.

1.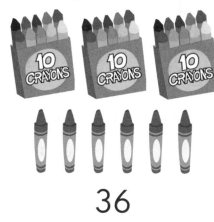

36   52

2.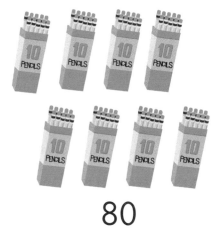

80   45

Compare the numbers. Write >, <, or = in the box.

3. 37 ☐ 73

4. 60 ☐ 16

5. 34 ☐ 34

6. 9 ☐ 32

7. 45 ☐ 49

8. 90 ☐ 69

T R Y   I T

Circle the number sentence that is true.

9. 25 > 26   14 < 12

38 > 37   49 < 45

10. 14 = 14   44 < 35

23 = 32   23 > 50

Compare the numbers. Write >, <, or = in the box.

11. 23 ☐ 34   **12.** 43 ☐ 33

13. 63 ☐ 61   **14.** 83 ☐ 93

Circle the correct symbol to compare the numbers.

15. 33 ☐ 73   **16.** 66 ☐ 16

$<$ $=$ $>$ $<$ $=$ $>$

17. 51 ☐ 51   **18.** 12 ☐ 21

$<$ $=$ $>$ $<$ $=$ $>$

T R Y   I T

Order Numbers Through 100

Order with Symbols

Write the numbers in order from least to greatest.

1. 45   76   70   ____ ____ ____

2. 35   15   88   ____ ____ ____

Write the numbers in order from greatest to least.

3. 44   50   91   ____ ____ ____

4. 52   25   67   ____ ____ ____

Write >, <, or = in the boxes to order the numbers.

5. 35 ☐ 77 ☐ 90   **6.** 64 ☐ 51 ☐ 33

7. 82 ☐ 37 ☐ 11   **8.** 10 ☐ 26 ☐ 81

T R Y   I T

Circle the symbols to order the numbers.

9. 96 ☐ 69 ☐ 55

     < <   = =   > >

Write >, <, or = in the boxes to order the numbers.

10. 61 ☐ 61 ☐ 61

11. 9 ☐ 10 ☐ 11

12. 75 ☐ 74 ☐ 73

13. 23 ☐ 32 ☐ 40

14. 81 ☐ 50 ☐ 45

15. 90 ☐ 80 ☐ 70

16. 40 ☐ 50 ☐ 60

17. 15 ☐ 25 ☐ 35

18. 65 ☐ 55 ☐ 50

TRY IT

Unit Review

Checkpoint Practice

1. Count aloud from 58 to 62. Then write the numbers on the lines.

> **Seats 58 to 62**

___,___,___,___,___

2. Count aloud from 96 to 100. Then write the numbers on the lines.

> **Seats 96 to 100**

___,___,___,___,___

Skip count to write the missing number.

3. 32, 34, 36, 38, _____

4. 20, 30, 40, 50, _____

5. 65, 70, 75, 80, _____

6. 40, 50, _____, 70, 80

7. 86, 88, 90, _____, 94

8. 40, 45, _____, 55, 60

Compare the numbers. Write >, <, or = in the box.

9. 61 ☐ 26

10. 39 ☐ 39

11. 46 ☐ 52

12. 73 ☐ 93

13. What number is this? Say it.

83

14. Count aloud from 65 to 80.

15. Write the number sixty-eight.

_____

16. Write the missing numbers.

40, _____ , 60, _____ , _____ , 90

17. Count by 5s. Circle the missing number.

55, 60, 65, 70, _____

A. 50   B. 75

C. 80   D. 71

18. Count by 2s. Circle the missing number.

42, 44, 46, 48, _____

A. 50   B. 49

C. 52   D. 58

19. Look at the numbers below. Which symbols belong in the boxes? Write the correct symbols.

61 ☐ 61 ☐ 61

20. Write the missing symbol in the box to compare the numbers.

36 ☐ 63

Time to the Nearest Hour

What Time Is It?

Circle the time to the nearest hour.

1.

2:00   8:00

2.

3:00   9:00

3.

5:00   4:00

4.

7:00   12:00

5.

3:00   2:00

6.

5:00   12:00

TRY IT

7. What time does the clock show? Say the answer.

8. Which clock shows 3:00? Circle the answer.

A.

B.

C.

D.

9. Which clock shows 8:00? Circle the answer.

A.

B.

C.

D.

10. What time does the clock show? Say the answer.

TRY IT

Time to the Nearest Half Hour

Tell Time to the Nearest Half Hour

Write the time that the clock shows.

1.

____:____

2.

____:____

3.

____:____

4.

____:____

5.

____:____

6.

____:____

Draw the hands of the clock to show the time.

7.

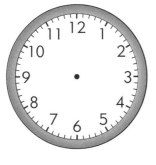

5:30

8.

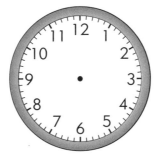

10:30

9.

8:30

TRY IT

Circle the answer.

10. Which clock shows 1:30?

A.  B.  C.

11. Which clock shows 2:30?

A.  B.  C.

What time does the clock show?

12.

A. 6:00

B. 6:30

C. 7:00

13.

A. 5:00

B. 4:00

C. 4:30

14. Which clock shows 4:30?

A.  B.  C.

15. Which clock shows 12:30?

A.  B.  C.

TRY IT

About Time

Tell Time and Relate Events

Draw a line to match each clock with the correct time to the nearest half hour.

1.

3:30

2.

12:30

3.

7:00

4.

5:30

5.

8:00

6.

11:00

T R Y   I T

Circle the answer.

7. About what time does the clock show?

A. 1:30   B. 1:00   C. 12:30

8. About what time does the clock show?

A. 7:00   B. 7:30   C. 8:00

9. Which clock shows 9:30?

A.   B.   C.

10. Which clock shows 8:30?

A.   B.   C.

Circle the activity that takes longer.

11.

Brushing your teeth   Playing a soccer game

12.

Watching a movie   Tying your shoes

Circle the activity that comes first.

13.

14.

TRY IT

15. Which activity would take the shortest amount of time?

    A. writing the word CHAIR

    B. writing the letter C

    C. writing the words CHAIR DESK LAMP

16. Which activity happens after the other two?

    A. going to sleep at night

    B. eating dinner

    C. brushing teeth before bed

17. Which activity do you do before getting out of bed?

    A. You brush your teeth.

    B. You wake up.

    C. You open the door.

18. Which do you do first when you want to read a book?

    A. You get the book.

    B. You start reading.

    C. You open the book.

TRY IT

Arrange and Describe Position

Arrange and Describe

Use the picture for Problems 1–4.

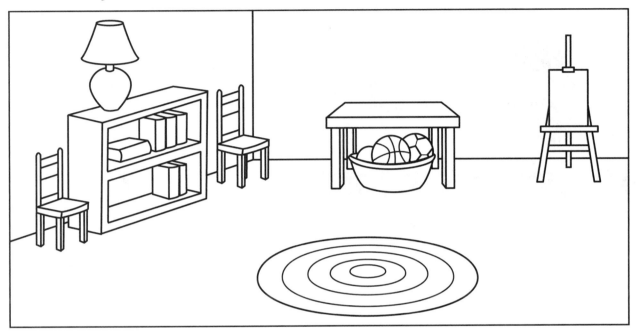

1. Circle the objects below the table in yellow.
2. Circle the objects near the bookcase in red.
3. Use a green crayon to draw a block above the table.
4. Use a blue crayon to draw a book far from the bookshelf.

Circle the answer.

5. You are standing in a room. Would you look up or down to see the floor?

   A. up   B. down

6. You are standing in a room. Would you look up or down to see the ceiling?

   A. up   B. down

TRY IT

7. Look at the picture. Where is the book?

    A. near the toy car
    B. under the toy car
    C. far from the toy car

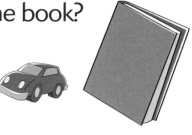

Use the picture for Problems 8–10. Circle the answer.

8. Which animal is far from the tree?

    A. bird   B. elephant   C. monkey

9. Which animal is above the elephant?

    A. monkey   B. mouse

10. Which way would you look to see the mouse?

    A. up   B. down

Use the picture for Problems 11 and 12. Circle the answer.

11. Which object is near the dog?

    A. bone   B. collar   C. ball

12. Which object is farthest from the dog?

    A. collar   B. bone   C. ball

TRY IT

Use Direction Words

Direction Words

Cut out each picture on the dotted lines. Glue the trees **to the left of** the pond. Glue the flowers **to the right of** the pond. Glue the bench **behind** the pond. Glue the duck **in front of** the pond.

LEARN

Use Direction Words

Arrange and Describe Objects

Look at the pair of objects. Color the object on the right green. Color the object on the left red.

1.

2.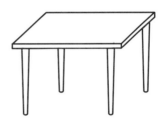

Look at the picture. Color the object in front green. Color the object behind blue.

3.

4.

Now draw another flower to the right of the flower.

TRY IT

Use the square for Problems 5 and 6.

5. Draw a circle to the left of the square.

6. Draw another square to the right of the square.

Circle the answer.

7. What is next to the doll?

    A. airplane

    B. books

    C. ball

    D. bear

8. What is in front of the books?

    A. bear

    B. ball

    C. airplane

    D. doll

9. What is to the left of the square?

    A. heart

    B. flower

10. What is to the right of the square?

    A. flower

    B. square

TRY IT

Unit Review

Checkpoint Practice

Write the time shown on the clock.

1.

_____ : _____

2.

_____ : _____

3.

_____ : _____

Circle the answer.

4. Which activity takes longer?

A.

B.

5. Which activity does the boy do after putting on his shoes?

A.

B.

Use the picture for Problems 6–9.

6. Circle the object that is far from the swing set.

7. Draw a rock near the tree.

8. Put an X on the object next to the swing set.

9. Draw a child in front of the swing set.

Circle the answer.

10. About what time does the clock show?

A. 1:00

B. 2:00

C. 3:00

11. About what time does the clock show?

A. 7:30

B. 6:30

C. 7:00

12. Which activity takes longest?

A. counting to 5

B. counting to 50

C. counting to 100

13. What is below the bed?

A. baseball   B. teddy bear   C. dresser

14. Where is the orange?

    A. below the table

    B. above the table

    C. next to the table

15. What is to the right of the train?

    A. teddy bear

    B. book

    C. baseball

16. What is behind the squirrel?

    A. bird

    B. acorns

    C. tree

Model Addition

What's the Sum?

Use yellow and blue cubes to find the sum. Then sketch the cubes and write the sum.

1. 7 plus 8

   _____

2. A group of 14 combined with a group of 12

   _____

3. 9 plus 13

   _____

T R Y   I T

4. Use yellow and blue cubes to find the total. Write the answer in the Total box.

Part	Part	Total
12	16	_____

5. Use yellow and blue cubes to find the total. Write the answer in the Total box.

Part	Part	Total
15	14	_____

Use yellow and blue cubes to find the sum. Then sketch the cubes and write the sum.

6. A group of 9 combined with a group of 8

_____

7. 6 plus 9

_____

8. Use yellow and blue cubes to find the total. Write the answer.

Part	Part	Total
8	15	_____

Add in Any Order

Meaning of Addition

Use blocks to show the bears. Then add. Write the sum.

1. There are 3 bears in the cave.
   There are 6 bears in the grass.

   How many bears are there in all? _____

2. There are 6 bears in the grass.
   There are 0 bears in the cave.

   How many bears are there in all? _____

LEARN

Use sketches to show the bears. Then add. Write the sum.

3. There are 7 black bears.
There are 5 brown bears.

How many bears are there in all? _____

Use blocks to show that the statement is true. Explain your answer.

4. Adding 9 and 6 is the same as adding 6 and 9.

Add in Any Order

Show Addition

Use blocks to show the problem. Then add.
Write the sum.

1. 8 red circles and 11 blue circles _____

2. 12 blue circles and 3 red circles _____

3. Tom and Pete each made a building out of blocks.
Tom started with 8 red blocks, and then added
2 blue blocks. Pete started with 2 blue blocks, and
then added 8 red blocks.

How many blocks did each
boy use in his building?   _____

How do you know? Say the answer.

TRY IT

Say the answer.

4. Is the sum of 8 and 4 the same as the sum of 4 and 8? Explain your answer.

Circle the answer.

5. Which is the same as 6 and 9?

   A. 6 and 5   B. 9 and 3   C. 9 and 6

6. You have 6 coins in your pocket. Your friend gives you 1 more. You now have 7 coins. Which best describes this situation?

   A. taking away   B. subtraction

   C. addition   D. making smaller

**Draw a picture to show how to solve the problem.
Then write the answer.**

7. Chris bought 9 baseball cards.
   Then he bought 4 more baseball cards.

   How many cards does he have now?   _____

The Plus Symbol

Write the Addition

Say the answer.

1. What is this symbol? $+$ What does it mean?

_____

2. What does $6 + 4$ mean?

Use numbers and the plus symbol to write an expression.

3.
  _____

4.
  _____

5.
  _____

6.
  _____

7. one plus seven

_____

8. three added to four

_____

TRY IT

Draw lines to match the models to the expressions.

9.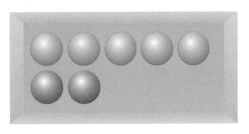

A. $6 + 1$

10.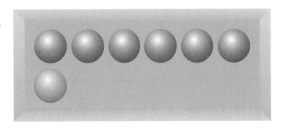

B. $8 + 0$

11.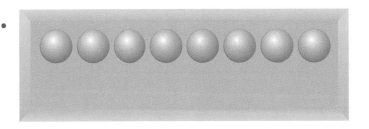

C. $2 + 4$

12.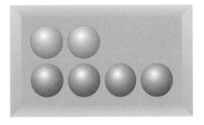

D. $5 + 2$

Draw a picture to show the expression.

13. $5 + 3$

14. $4 + 1$

Circle the answer.

15. What does the symbol the arrow is pointing to mean?

$$11 \downarrow + 4 = 15$$

A. add   B. equals   C. subtract

---

16. Which problem shows how to add the balls?

A. $2 + 6$ B. $5 + 4$

C. $4 + 3$ D. $5 + 2$

Read the problem and follow the directions.

17. Use craft sticks to model this expression: $6 + 4$. Then show how to find the sum.

18. Use numbers and the plus symbol to write an expression for the model.

_____

19. Complete the sentence by writing the correct symbol in the box.

The total of 10 ⬜ 5 is 15.

20. Complete the sentence by writing the correct symbol in the box.

The total of 5 ⬜ 4 is 9.

TRY IT

The Equals Symbol

What Is the Equals Symbol?

Say the answer.

1. What is this symbol?

$$=$$

2. What does $=$ mean?

3. What does $2 + 6 = 8$ mean?

Write an equals symbol if the two sides are equal.
Write a not-equal-to symbol if the two sides are
not equal.

4. $9 \boxed{} 3 + 5$

5. $9 + 8 \boxed{} 17$

6. $9 + 1 \boxed{} 10$

7. $15 \boxed{} 10 + 5$

8. $14 \boxed{} 7 + 7$

9. $4 + 9 \boxed{} 15$

10. $20 \boxed{} 13 + 6$

11. $7 + 12 \boxed{} 19$

TRY IT

Circle the answer.

12. Which number belongs in the box?

$$8 = \boxed{} + 4$$

A. 2   B. 4   C. 8   D. 12

13. Which number belongs in the box?

$$7 + \boxed{} = 9$$

A. 1   B. 2   C. 3   D. 4

14. Which symbol belongs in the box?

$$7 + 2 \boxed{} 9$$

A. +   B. >   C. −   D. =

Write the answer.

15. What number belongs in the box?

$$9 + 9 = \boxed{}$$

16. Look at this number sentence: $5 = 3 + 2$.
What does the equals symbol mean in this
number sentence?

TRY IT

Number Sentences: The Equals Symbol

Make Number Sentences

Write the number sentence shown. Use $=$ or $\neq$.

1.

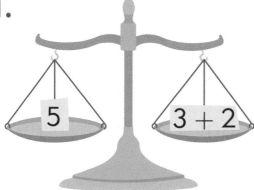

_____

2.

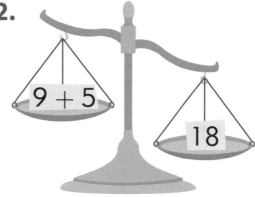

_____

3.

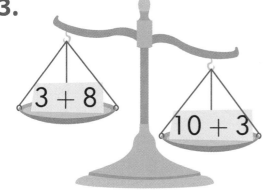

_____

4.

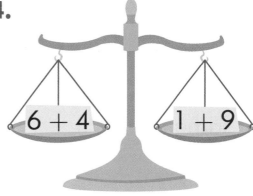

_____

Write an addition expression to complete the number sentence.

5. $4 =$ _____

6. $4 + 3 =$ _____

TRY IT

Write a number sentence for the problem.

7. 12 is the same as 4 plus 8. _____

8. 7 added to 6 is the same as 5 added to 8.

_____

9. 3 added to 7 is the same as 1 added to 9.

_____

10. Write an addition sentence that uses the numbers 3, 5, and 8, and the equals symbol.

_____

11. Write an addition sentence that uses the numbers 4, 6, and 2, and the equals symbol.

_____

12. Write a number sentence that shows that 7 is the same as $3 + 4$.

_____

13. Write a number sentence that shows that 13 is the same as $9 + 4$.

_____

Write $=$ or $\neq$ in the box.

14. $4 + 6$ ☐ 11

15. 8 ☐ $7 + 1$

Unit Review

Checkpoint Practice

Read the problem and follow the directions.

1. Model the problem with yellow and red circles. Sketch your circles. Then write the sum.

   There are 4 puppies in a basket.
   There are 6 puppies on the rug.

   How many puppies are there in all?   _____

2. Use 11 yellow circles and 3 red circles to explain addition.

3. Use circles to show that 4 plus 9 is the same as 9 plus 4.

4. Use the number line to show that 8 plus 4 is the same as 4 plus 8.

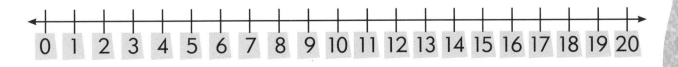

5. Explain what the expression $4 + 7$ means. Be sure to explain what the symbol means.

Write an equals symbol in the box if the two sides are equal. Write a not-equal-to symbol if they are not equal.

6. $10\ \boxed{}\ 5 + 5$

7. $8 + 4\ \boxed{}\ 12$

8. $7 + 4\ \boxed{}\ 10$

9. $3 + 9\ \boxed{}\ 11$

Complete the number sentence. Write a number or symbol.

10. $4 = \underline{\hspace{1.5cm}}$

11. $\underline{\hspace{1.5cm}} = 8 + 3$

12. $4 + 3 = \underline{\hspace{1.5cm}}$

13. $3 + 4 \underline{\hspace{1.5cm}} 2 + 5$

Write a number sentence.

14. 7 added to 8 is the same as 10 added to 5. $\underline{\hspace{4cm}}$

15. 16 is the same as 5 plus 11. $\underline{\hspace{4cm}}$

16. 9 added to 3 is the same as 12. $\underline{\hspace{4cm}}$

Read the problem and follow the directions.

17. What does the symbol the arrow is pointing to mean? Circle the answer.

$$4 + 2 \overset{\downarrow}{=} 6$$

   A. add   B. equals   C. subtract

18. Circle the symbol that belongs in the box.

$$12 \boxed{} 10 + 2$$

   A. $+$ B. $-$ C. $=$ D. $\neq$

19. Write $=$ or $\neq$ in the box.

$$14 \boxed{} 7 + 7$$

20. Is $11 + 30$ the same as $30 + 11$? Explain.

21. Use red and yellow circles to show how to add $5 + 10$.

22. Write a number sentence for this model:

●●●●●●●● + ●●●●● = ●●●●●●●●●●●●●

_____

23. Diane bought 4 oranges. Then she bought 5 more oranges.

How many oranges does she have now? _____

Draw a picture that shows how to solve this.

24. This morning you read 2 books. This evening you read 2 more books. You read a total of 4 books.

Which tells how you read a total of 4 books? Circle the answer.

A. Two groups were compared.

B. Two groups were taken apart.

C. Two groups were joined together.

25. Circle the addition symbol in this number sentence.

$$30 = 28 + 2$$

26. Complete the number sentence. Circle the answer.

$$11 \boxed{} 1 = 12$$

A. −   B. =   C. +

Name: _____

Write the sum.

1. $6 + 2 =$ _____

2. $0 + 3 =$ _____

3. _____ $= 4 + 1$

4. $3 + 3 =$ _____

5.
$$\begin{array}{r} 1 \\ + 2 \\ \hline \end{array}$$

6.
$$\begin{array}{r} 4 \\ + 4 \\ \hline \end{array}$$

7.
$$\begin{array}{r} 6 \\ + 0 \\ \hline \end{array}$$

8.
$$\begin{array}{r} 5 \\ + 2 \\ \hline \end{array}$$

Write numbers in the boxes to make the number sentence true.

9. ☐ + ☐ = 7

10. ☐ + ☐ = 5

11.
$$\begin{array}{r} \square \\ + \square \\ \hline 6 \end{array}$$

12.
$$\begin{array}{r} \square \\ + \square \\ \hline 4 \end{array}$$

TRY IT

Say the answer.

13. What is the sum when you add zero to any number?

Circle the answer.

14. $0 + 7 = ?$

    A. 70   B. 8

    C. 7   D. 17

15.
$$\begin{array}{r} 0 \\ + 5 \\ \hline \end{array}$$

    A. 15   B. 5

    C. 6   D. 50

16.
$$\begin{array}{r} 2 \\ + 3 \\ \hline \end{array}$$

    A. 1   B. 4

    C. 5   D. 6

17.
$$\begin{array}{r} 3 \\ + 4 \\ \hline \end{array}$$

    A. 7   B. 6

    C. 5   D. 1

18.
$$\begin{array}{r} 3 \\ + 3 \\ \hline \end{array}$$

    A. 0   B. 3

    C. 5   D. 6

19. $2 + 2 = ?$

    A. 0   B. 2

    C. 3   D. 4

20. $3 + 1 = ?$

    A. 4   B. 3

    C. 2   D. 1

21. $1 + 4 = ?$

    A. 3   B. 4

    C. 5   D. 6

Sums Through 8

Number Facts

Write the sum.

1. $5 + 3 =$ _____

2. $3 + 4 =$ _____

3. _____ $= 3 + 3$

4. _____ $= 0 + 7$

5.
$$\begin{array}{r} 2 \\ + 6 \\ \hline \end{array}$$

6.
$$\begin{array}{r} 2 \\ + 3 \\ \hline \end{array}$$

7. Fill in all the blanks to make true number sentences. All of the number sentences should be different.

_____ $+$ _____ $= 5$

_____ $+$ _____ $= 5$

_____ $+$ _____ $= 5$

_____ $+$ _____ $= 5$

_____ $+$ _____ $= 5$

_____ $+$ _____ $= 5$

TRY IT

Write the sum.

8.   0
      $+\ 6$

9.   3
      $+\ 0$

10.   0
       $+\ 0$

Circle the answer.

11. $5 + 2 = ?$

A. 2   B. 5

C. 6   D. 7

12. $4 + 4 = ?$

A. 0   B. 4

C. 7   D. 8

13. $2 + 4 = ?$

A. 7   B. 6

C. 4   D. 2

Write the sum.

14.   5
       $+\ 3$

15.   6
       $+\ 2$

16.   1
       $+\ 1$

Facts Through 12

Practice Number Facts

Write the sum.

1. $9 + 1 =$ _____

2. _____ $= 2 + 4$

3. _____ $= 0 + 11$

4. $5 + 2 =$ _____

5. $\begin{array}{r} 2 \\ + 7 \\ \hline \end{array}$

6. $\begin{array}{r} 6 \\ + 5 \\ \hline \end{array}$

7. $\begin{array}{r} 4 \\ + 8 \\ \hline \end{array}$

8. $\begin{array}{r} 3 \\ + 6 \\ \hline \end{array}$

9. Fill in the blank to make the number sentence true.

$0 +$ _____ $= 10$ $\qquad$ $6 +$ _____ $= 10$

$1 +$ _____ $= 10$ $\qquad$ $7 +$ _____ $= 10$

$2 +$ _____ $= 10$ $\qquad$ $8 +$ _____ $= 10$

$3 +$ _____ $= 10$ $\qquad$ $9 +$ _____ $= 10$

$4 +$ _____ $= 10$ $\qquad$ $10 +$ _____ $= 10$

$5 +$ _____ $= 10$

TRY IT

Write the sum.

10. $5 + 6 =$ _____

11. $9 + 1 =$ _____

12. _____ $= 7 + 5$

13. $3 + 9 =$ _____

Circle the answer.

14.
$$\begin{array}{r} 10 \\ +\ 0 \\ \hline \end{array}$$

A. 11   B. 10

C. 9   D. 0

15.
$$\begin{array}{r} 6 \\ +\ 3 \\ \hline \end{array}$$

A. 3   B. 6

C. 8   D. 9

16.
$$\begin{array}{r} 7 \\ +\ 4 \\ \hline \end{array}$$

A. 3   B. 7

C. 11   D. 12

17.
$$\begin{array}{r} 3 \\ +\ 8 \\ \hline \end{array}$$

A. 12   B. 11

C. 10   D. 5

18.
$$\begin{array}{r} 10 \\ +\ 2 \\ \hline \end{array}$$

A. 8   B. 10

C. 12   D. 13

TRY IT

Sums Through 12

Only the Facts

Write the sum.

1. $6 + 3 =$ _____

2. _____ $= 7 + 4$

3. _____ $= 3 + 6$

4. $10 + 2 =$ _____

5. $\begin{array}{r} 8 \\ +\ 2 \\ \hline \end{array}$

6. $\begin{array}{r} 6 \\ +\ 6 \\ \hline \end{array}$

7. $\begin{array}{r} 0 \\ +\ 12 \\ \hline \end{array}$

8. $\begin{array}{r} 9 \\ +\ 2 \\ \hline \end{array}$

9. $\begin{array}{r} 6 \\ +\ 2 \\ \hline \end{array}$

10. $\begin{array}{r} 5 \\ +\ 4 \\ \hline \end{array}$

11. Read the addition facts shown to you on the flash cards. Say each sum as quickly as you can. You will have 1 minute to complete 20 facts.

TRY IT

Circle the answer.

12. $5 + 7 = ?$

    A. 2   B. 11   C. 12   D. 13

13. $2 + 9 = ?$

    A. 12   B. 11   C. 10   D. 7

14. $9 + 3 = ?$

    A. 12   B. 11   C. 10   D. 6

Write the sum.

15. $5 + 6 =$ _____

16. $4 + 5 =$ _____

17. $2 + 8 =$ _____

18. $\begin{array}{r} 7 \\ + 5 \\ \hline \end{array}$

19. $\begin{array}{r} 8 \\ + 4 \\ \hline \end{array}$

Unit Review

Checkpoint Practice

Write the sum.

1. $2 + 3 =$ _____

2. _____ $= 0 + 2$

3. $7 + 1 =$ _____

4. $3 + 3 =$ _____

5.
$$\begin{array}{r} 1 \\ + \ 2 \\ \hline \end{array}$$

6.
$$\begin{array}{r} 3 \\ + \ 4 \\ \hline \end{array}$$

7.
$$\begin{array}{r} 4 \\ + \ 0 \\ \hline \end{array}$$

8.
$$\begin{array}{r} 6 \\ + \ 2 \\ \hline \end{array}$$

9. $3 + 9 =$ _____

10. _____ $= 4 + 6$

11. _____ $= 7 + 2$

12. $4 + 7 =$ _____

13.
$$\begin{array}{r} 1 \\ + \ 8 \\ \hline \end{array}$$

14.
$$\begin{array}{r} 3 \\ + \ 7 \\ \hline \end{array}$$

15.
$$\begin{array}{r} 5 \\ + \ 6 \\ \hline \end{array}$$

16.
$$\begin{array}{r} 7 \\ + \ 5 \\ \hline \end{array}$$

UNIT REVIEW

Circle the answer.

17. $0 + 12 = ?$

    A. 012   B. 120

    C. 12   D. 13

18. $11 + 0 = ?$

    A. 110   B. 11

    C. 011   D. 12

Write the sum.

19. $3 + 5 = $ _____

20. $5 + 7 = $ _____

21. $4 + 3 = $ _____

22. $6 + 3 = $ _____

23.
$$\begin{array}{r} 9 \\ + 1 \\ \hline \end{array}$$

24.
$$\begin{array}{r} 3 \\ + 9 \\ \hline \end{array}$$

Circle the answer.

25.
$$\begin{array}{r} 6 \\ + 5 \\ \hline \end{array}$$

    A. 9   B. 10

    C. 11   D. 12

26.
$$\begin{array}{r} 4 \\ + 7 \\ \hline \end{array}$$

    A. 12   B. 11

    C. 7   D. 4

UNIT REVIEW

Facts Through 16

Know the Facts

Write the sum.

1. $8 + 3 =$ _____

2. _____ $= 5 + 8$

3. $7 + 6 =$ _____

4. $7 + 7 =$ _____

5.
$$\begin{array}{r} 8 \\ +\ 6 \\ \hline \end{array}$$

6.
$$\begin{array}{r} 9 \\ +\ 7 \\ \hline \end{array}$$

7.
$$\begin{array}{r} 6 \\ +\ 9 \\ \hline \end{array}$$

8.
$$\begin{array}{r} 5 \\ +\ 4 \\ \hline \end{array}$$

9.
$$\begin{array}{r} 3 \\ +\ 7 \\ \hline \end{array}$$

10.
$$\begin{array}{r} 7 \\ +\ 8 \\ \hline \end{array}$$

11. Fill in the blank to make the number sentence true.

$6 +$ _____ $= 16$

$9 +$ _____ $= 16$

$7 +$ _____ $= 16$

$10 +$ _____ $= 16$

$8 +$ _____ $= 16$

TRY IT

Circle the answer.

12.   10
          $\underline{+\ 3}$

   A. 7   B. 11

   C. 12   D. 13

13.   13
          $\underline{+\ 3}$

   A. 17   B. 16

   C. 14   D. 10

14.   12
          $\underline{+\ 3}$

   A. 12   B. 14

   C. 15   D. 16

15.   14
          $\underline{+\ 1}$

   A. 12   B. 13

   C. 14   D. 15

16. $12 + 2 = ?$

   A. 10   B. 12

   C. 13   D. 14

17. $14 + 1 = ?$

   A. 15   B. 14

   C. 13   D. 12

18. $0 + 15 = ?$

   A. 0   B. 15

   C. 16   D. 17

19. $11 + 5 = ?$

   A. 16   B. 15

   C. 11   D. 6

TRY IT

Sums Through 16

Fact Sums

Write the sum.

1. $6 + 8 =$ _____

2. _____ $= 9 + 4$

3. _____ $= 7 + 8$

4. $10 + 6 =$ _____

5.
$$\begin{array}{r} 8 \\ +\ 3 \\ \hline \end{array}$$

6.
$$\begin{array}{r} 5 \\ +\ 7 \\ \hline \end{array}$$

7.
$$\begin{array}{r} 0 \\ +10 \\ \hline \end{array}$$

8.
$$\begin{array}{r} 9 \\ +\ 7 \\ \hline \end{array}$$

9.
$$\begin{array}{r} 6 \\ +\ 7 \\ \hline \end{array}$$

10.
$$\begin{array}{r} 9 \\ +\ 6 \\ \hline \end{array}$$

TRY IT

Circle the answer.

11.   14
       + 2

   A. 16   B. 15

   C. 14   D. 12

12.   13
       + 0

   A. 14   B. 13

   C. 12   D. 11

13. $13 + 1 = ?$

   A. 12   B. 13

   C. 14   D. 15

14. $4 + 11 = ?$

   A. 7   B. 13

   C. 14   D. 15

15. $1 + 15 = ?$

   A. 1   B. 15

   C. 16   D. 17

Write the sum.

16.   7
        + 7

17.   8
        + 8

18. $8 + 6 =$ _____

TRY IT

Facts Through 20

Flower Facts

Cut out each flower, petal, and leaf. Group the leaves and petals that have the same sum. Then glue them to the flower with that sum.

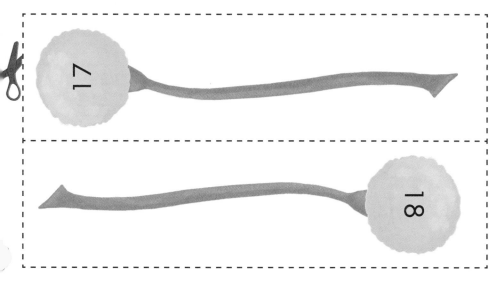

17

18

| $8 + 9$ | $10 + 8$ | $11 + 8$ | $12 + 8$ | $10 + 7$ |

| $15 + 3$ | $7 + 12$ | $15 + 2$ | $9 + 9$ |

| $15 + 4$ | $15 + 5$ | $12 + 5$ | $4 + 14$ |

LEARN

Cut out each flower, petal, and leaf. Group the leaves and petals that have the same sum. Then glue them to the flower with that sum.

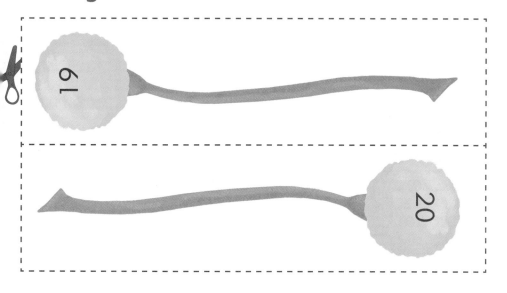

19

20

6 + 12   10 + 9   10 + 10   7 + 13   6 + 11

14 + 5   6 + 14   4 + 13   0 + 18

3 + 16   9 + 11   17 + 0   11 + 7

19 + 0   0 + 20

Facts Through 20

Sum It Up

Write the sum.

1. $10 + 8 =$ _____

2. _____ $= 5 + 8$

3. _____ $= 7 + 1$

4. $10 + 10 =$ _____

5. $10 + 9 =$ _____

6. $7 + 10 =$ _____

7.
$$\begin{array}{r} 6 \\ + 7 \\ \hline \end{array}$$

8.
$$\begin{array}{r} 9 \\ + 8 \\ \hline \end{array}$$

9.
$$\begin{array}{r} 8 \\ + 0 \\ \hline \end{array}$$

10.
$$\begin{array}{r} 9 \\ + 9 \\ \hline \end{array}$$

TRY IT

11.
$$\begin{array}{r} 4 \\ + \ 4 \\ \hline \end{array}$$

12.
$$\begin{array}{r} 7 \\ + \ 6 \\ \hline \end{array}$$

13.
$$\begin{array}{r} 10 \\ + \ 7 \\ \hline \end{array}$$

14.
$$\begin{array}{r} 8 \\ + \ 9 \\ \hline \end{array}$$

15. $9 + 8 = $ _____

16. $10 + 6 = $ _____

17. $3 + 6 = $ _____

18. $10 + 8 = $ _____

19. $4 + 9 = $ _____

20. $8 + 8 = $ _____

Sums Through 20

All Sums

Write the sum.

1. $10 + 10 =$ _____

2. _____ $= 6 + 9$

3. _____ $= 7 + 5$

4. $7 + 7 =$ _____

5. $20 + 0 =$ _____

6. $10 + 9 =$ _____

7.
$$\begin{array}{r} 9 \\ + 7 \\ \hline \end{array}$$

8.
$$\begin{array}{r} 9 \\ + 8 \\ \hline \end{array}$$

9.
$$\begin{array}{r} 8 \\ + 5 \\ \hline \end{array}$$

10.
$$\begin{array}{r} 9 \\ + 9 \\ \hline \end{array}$$

TRY IT

Circle the answer.

11. $5 + 10 = ?$

    A. 5   B. 14

    C. 15   D. 16

12. $9 + 6 = ?$

    A. 15   B. 16

    C. 14   D. 13

13. $10 + 7 = ?$

    A. 8   B. 12

    C. 15   D. 17

14. $7 + 0 = ?$

    A. 8   B. 7

    C. 6   D. 0

Write the sum.

15.
$$\begin{array}{r} 10 \\ + 6 \\ \hline \end{array}$$

16.
$$\begin{array}{r} 9 \\ + 5 \\ \hline \end{array}$$

17.
$$\begin{array}{r} 8 \\ + 5 \\ \hline \end{array}$$

18.
$$\begin{array}{r} 5 \\ + 5 \\ \hline \end{array}$$

TRY IT

Unit Review

Checkpoint Practice

Problems 1–20 are timed. You will have 3 minutes and 30 seconds to complete this section. Write the sum.

1. 8
   $+ 6$

2. 9
   $+ 6$

3. 3
   $+ 0$

4. 8
   $+ 4$

5. 8
   $+ 2$

6. $5 + 7 =$ _____

7. $5 + 3 =$ _____

8. $0 + 4 =$ _____

9. $9 + 0 =$ _____

10. $6 + 4 =$ _____

11. $9 + 1 =$ _____

12. $10 + 0 =$ _____

13. $7 + 2 =$ _____

14. $6 + 8 =$ _____

15. $3 + 5 =$ _____

16. 10
    $+ 4$

17. 9
    $+ 7$

18. 8
    $+ 7$

19. 9
    $+ 9$

20. 8
    $+ 0$

UNIT REVIEW

This section is untimed. Write the sum.

1. $7 + 9 =$ _____

2. _____ $= 6 + 3$

3. _____ $= 9 + 1$

4. $5 + 5 =$ _____

5.
$$\begin{array}{r} 6 \\ +\ 5 \\ \hline \end{array}$$

6.
$$\begin{array}{r} 7 \\ +\ 7 \\ \hline \end{array}$$

7.
$$\begin{array}{r} 3 \\ +\ 8 \\ \hline \end{array}$$

8.
$$\begin{array}{r} 8 \\ +\ 6 \\ \hline \end{array}$$

9. $4 + 8 =$ _____

10. _____ $= 10 + 10$

11. _____ $= 9 + 3$

12. $7 + 8 =$ _____

13.
$$\begin{array}{r} 6 \\ +\ 9 \\ \hline \end{array}$$

14.
$$\begin{array}{r} 8 \\ +\ 8 \\ \hline \end{array}$$

15.
$$\begin{array}{r} 9 \\ +\ 8 \\ \hline \end{array}$$

16.
$$\begin{array}{r} 9 \\ +\ 9 \\ \hline \end{array}$$

Circle the answer.

17. $10 + 6 = ?$

    A. 17   B. 16

    C. 15   D. 14

18. $6 + 7 = ?$

    A. 15   B. 13

    C. 7   D. 6

19.
$$\begin{array}{r} 7 \\ + 7 \\ \hline \end{array}$$

    A. 18   B. 14

    C. 12   D. 10

20.
$$\begin{array}{r} 8 \\ + 3 \\ \hline \end{array}$$

    A. 14   B. 13

    C. 11   D. 9

21.
$$\begin{array}{r} 4 \\ + 3 \\ \hline \end{array}$$

    A. 5   B. 6

    C. 7   D. 8

22.
$$\begin{array}{r} 6 \\ + 6 \\ \hline \end{array}$$

    A. 12   B. 13

    C. 14   D. 15

23.
$$\begin{array}{r} 8 \\ + 7 \\ \hline \end{array}$$

    A. 10   B. 13

    C. 15   D. 17

24.
$$\begin{array}{r} 10 \\ + 7 \\ \hline \end{array}$$

    A. 17   B. 16

    C. 15   D. 14

25.
$$\begin{array}{r} 8 \\ + 8 \\ \hline \end{array}$$

    A. 18   B. 16

    C. 14   D. 12

26.
$$\begin{array}{r} 9 \\ + 7 \\ \hline \end{array}$$

    A. 12   B. 15

    C. 16   D. 19

Write the sum.

27. $10 + 2 =$ _____

28. $9 + 2 =$ _____

29. $8 + 1 =$ _____

30. $8 + 9 =$ _____

31.
$$\begin{array}{r} 5 \\ + 9 \\ \hline \end{array}$$

32.
$$\begin{array}{r} 7 \\ + 3 \\ \hline \end{array}$$

33.
$$\begin{array}{r} 4 \\ + 4 \\ \hline \end{array}$$

34. $2 + 10 =$ _____

35. $10 + 4 =$ _____

36. $10 + 10 =$ _____

One More, 10 More

One More on a Number Line

Use the number lines to find the answers.

1.

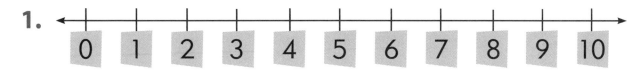

What number is 1 more than 5? _____

2.

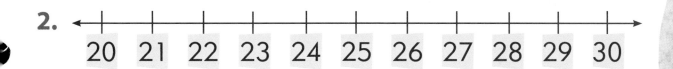

What number is 1 more than 27? _____

3.

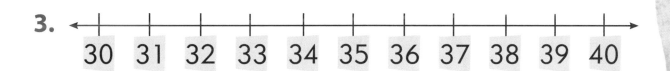

What number is 1 more than 34? _____

LEARN

4.

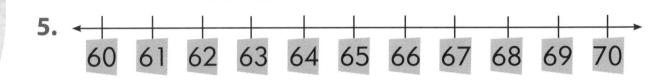

What number is 1 more than 53? _____

5.

What number is 1 more than 68? _____

6.

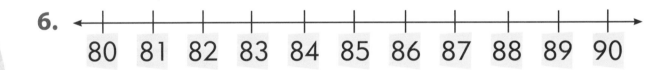

What number is 1 more than 89? _____

One More, 10 More

One More and 10 More

Use the number lines to find the answers.

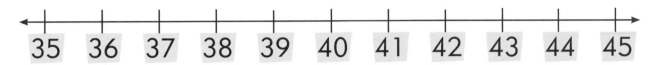

35   36   37   38   39   40   41   42   43   44   45

1. What number is 1 more than 38? _____

2. What number is 1 more than 42? _____

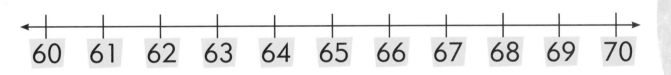

60   61   62   63   64   65   66   67   68   69   70

3. What number is 1 more than 61? _____

4. What number is 1 more than 69? _____

Write the number that is 1 more than
the given number.

5. 95 _____   **6.** 18 _____   **7.** 79 _____

T R Y   I T

Circle the answer.

8. What number is 1 more than 15?

    A. 12   B. 16   C. 14   D. 19

9. What number is 1 more than 37?

    A. 36   B. 38   C. 40   D. 42

10. What number is 1 more than 12?

    A. 10   B. 11   C. 12   D. 13

11. What number is 1 more than 19?

    A. 20   B. 21   C. 18   D. 17

12. What number is 1 more than 7?

    A. 7   B. 8   C. 9   D. 10

13. What number is 1 more than 23?

    A. 24   B. 26   C. 27   D. 28

TRY IT

Use this half of the hundred chart for Problems 14–17.

1	2	3	4	5	6	7	8	9	10
11	12	13	14	15	16	17	18	19	20
21	22	23	24	25	26	27	28	29	30
31	32	33	34	35	36	37	38	39	40
41	42	43	44	45	46	47	48	49	50

14. What number is 10 more than 39? _____

15. What number is 10 more than 26? _____

16. What number is 10 more than 4? _____

17. What number is 10 more than 40? _____

TRY IT

Write the number that is 10 more than the given number.

18. 44 _____   **19.** 8 _____   **20.** 79 _____

Use the number lines to find the answers.

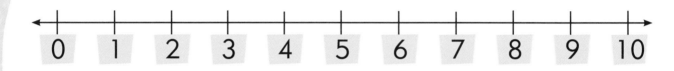

21. 10 is 1 more than what number? _____

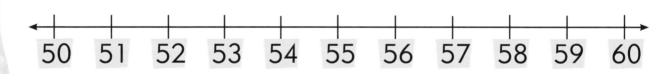

22. 60 is 10 more than what number? _____

Count On to Add

Practice Counting on a Number Line

Use the number line to count on to find the sum.

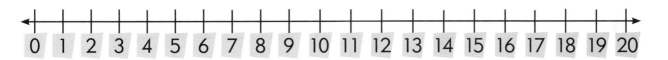

1. $5 + 3 =$ _____

2. $4 + 9 =$ _____

3. $11 + 8 =$ _____

4. $0 + 16 =$ _____

5. $2 + 13 =$ _____

6. $15 + 5 =$ _____

7. $12 + 7 =$ _____

8. $4 + 12 =$ _____

9. $9 + 4 =$ _____

TRY IT

Use the number line to count on to find the sum.

$$\underset{\text{0 1 2 3 4 5 6 7 8 9 10 11 12 13 14 15 16 17 18 19 20}}{\longleftrightarrow}$$

10. $6 + 5 =$ _____

11. _____ $= 8 + 4$

12. $12 + 5 =$ _____

13. _____ $= 0 + 15$

14. _____ $= 3 + 14$

15. $16 + 3 =$ _____

16. $14 + 4 =$ _____

17. $5 + 13 =$ _____

18. $7 + 6 =$ _____

Count On to Add

Use Blocks to Count On

Count on to find the sum.
Use circles to help you.

1. $5 + 2 =$ _____

2. $4 + 5 =$ _____

3. $7 + 8 =$ _____

4. $0 + 9 =$ _____

5. $2 + 12 =$ _____

6. $16 + 3 =$ _____

7. $10 + 7 =$ _____

8. $4 + 15 =$ _____

L E A R N

9. $7 + 2 =$ _____

10. _____ $= 12 + 5$

11. _____ $= 7 + 4$

12. $1 + 8 =$ _____

13. $3 + 13 =$ _____

14. $15 + 4 =$ _____

15. _____ $= 10 + 9$

16. $3 + 14 =$ _____

LEARN

Count On to Add

Use Strategies to Add

Choose a strategy to find the sum.
Explain which strategy you chose for the problem.

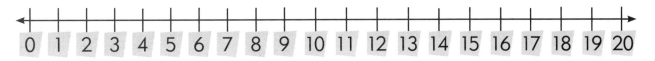

1. $6 + 7 =$ _____

2. $6 + 9 =$ _____

3. $10 + 8 =$ _____

4. $3 + 5 =$ _____

5. $8 + 9 =$ _____

6. $8 + 7 =$ _____

7. $5 + 5 =$ _____

8. $8 + 6 =$ _____

9. $9 + 5 =$ _____

LEARN

10. $5 + 8 =$ _____

11. _____ $= 7 + 8$

12. $9 + 7 =$ _____

13. _____ $= 4 + 7$

14. $9 + 9 =$ _____

15. _____ $= 5 + 7$

16. $7 + 7 =$ _____

17. _____ $= 7 + 6$

18. $9 + 4 =$ _____

Count On to Add

Solve Addition Problems

Use the number line to count on to find the sum.

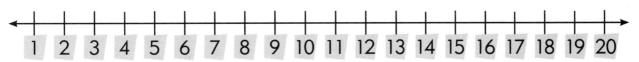

1. $2 + 8 =$ _____

2. $11 + 6 =$ _____

3. $7 + 4 =$ _____

4. $14 + 5 =$ _____

Count on to find the sum.

5. $16 + 4 =$ _____

6. $5 + 7 =$ _____

7. $10 + 5 =$ _____

Use any strategy you have learned to find the sum.

8. $6 + 9 =$ _____

9. $18 + 3 =$ _____

10. $25 + 4 =$ _____

TRY IT

Use the number line to count on to find the sum.

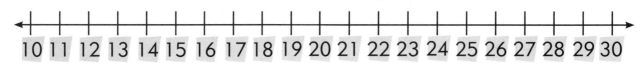

10 11 12 13 14 15 16 17 18 19 20 21 22 23 24 25 26 27 28 29 30

11. $17 + 10 = $ _____

12. $13 + 5 = $ _____

13. $16 + 5 = $ _____

14. Use a strategy you have learned, or math facts, to solve this problem. Then explain how you solved the problem.

$9 + 6 = $ _____

15. Use a strategy you have learned, or math facts, to solve this problem. Circle the answer.

$$7 + 4 = ?$$

A. 13   B. 12   C. 11   D. 10

16. Count on 9 from 13 to find the sum of $13 + 9$.

$13 + 9 = $ _____

TRY IT

Different Ways to Add

Addition Strategies

Use the number line to count on to find the sum.

10 11 12 13 14 15 16 17 18 19 20 21 22 23 24 25 26 27 28 29 30

1. $10 + 6 =$ _____

2. $23 + 5 =$ _____

3. $15 + 4 =$ _____

4. $16 + 9 =$ _____

Count on to find the sum.

5. $23 + 4 =$ _____

6. $6 + 15 =$ _____

7. $26 + 3 =$ _____

Use any strategy you have learned to find the sum.

8. $17 + 2 =$ _____

9. $21 + 9 =$ _____

10. $19 + 6 =$ _____

TRY IT

Count on from the greater number to find the sum. Circle the answer.

11. $12 + 3 = ?$

    A. 15   B. 16   C. 17

12. Using the number line, count to solve $18 + 10$.

    A. 28   B. 18   C. 24

Use the number line to count on to find the sum.

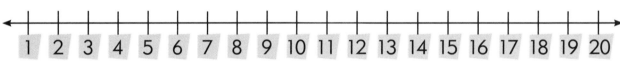

13. $4 + 15 =$ _____

Use an addition strategy to find the sum.
Explain how you solved the problem.

14. $15 + 5 =$ _____   **15.** $8 + 9 =$ _____

16. Coleman has 4 cookies. His friend gives him 5 more. Count on from 4 to find how many cookies Coleman has in all.

_____

Grouping to Add

Plate Addition

Use cubes to show three different ways to make the number. Make drawings to show your ways.

Example: Ways to Make 9

Way 1

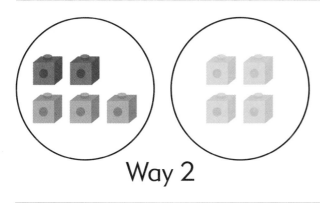

Way 2

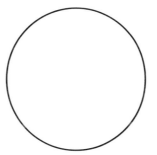 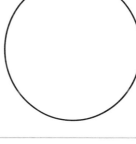

Way 3

---

1. Ways to Make 16

Way 1

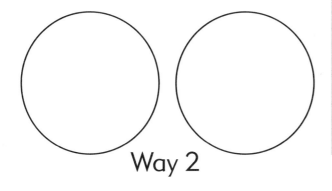

Way 2

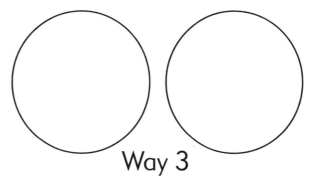

Way 3

LEARN

2. Ways to Make 13

Way 1

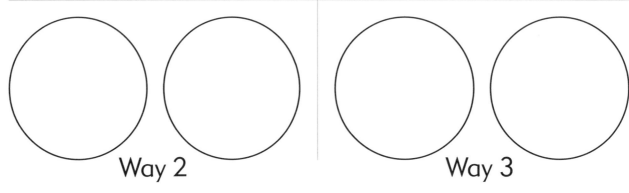

Way 2   Way 3

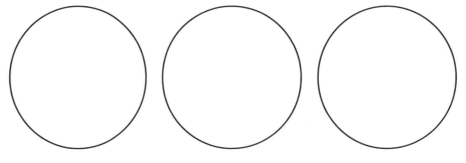

3. Ways to Make 15

Way 1

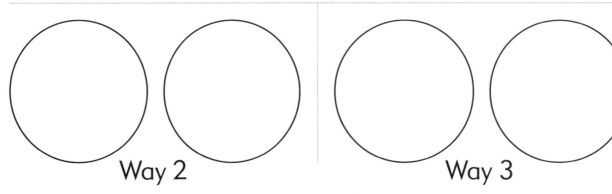

Way 2   Way 3

Grouping to Add
Group to Add

Draw hearts in the circles to show how to combine the groups to show the total in two other ways.

1. 7

Way 1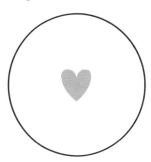

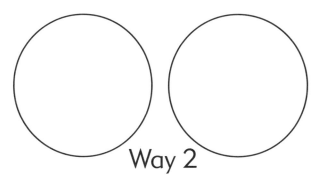 Way 2   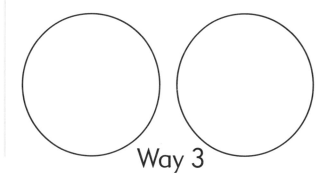 Way 3

2. 9

Way 1

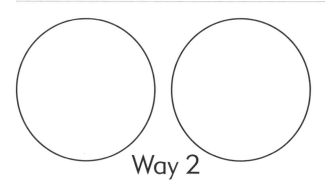 Way 2   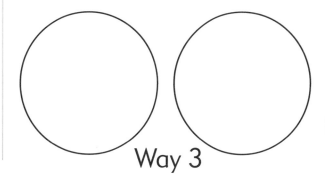 Way 3

TRY IT

For Problems 3–5, first make three groups of cubes to show the number. Then combine the groups in two different ways to show the number again.

Example: 11

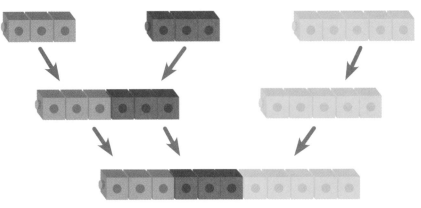

3. 6	**4.** 8	**5.** 12

6. Draw stars in the circles to show a total of 7 stars:

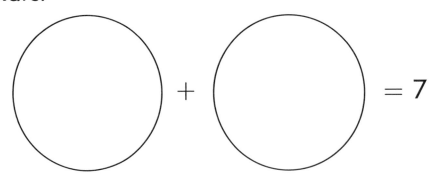

Now draw stars in the circles to show a total of 7 stars in a different way:

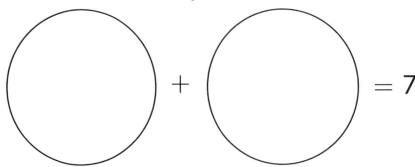

Grouping to Add

Add Three Numbers

Find the sum. First add the two addends that are circled. Then add the third addend to their sum.

Example:

$(9 + 1) + 2 = \underline{12}$

1. $9 + (1 + 2) = \underline{\hspace{1cm}}$

2.
$$\begin{array}{r} (3 \\ 6) \\ + \ 8 \\ \hline \end{array}$$

3.
$$\begin{array}{r} 3 \\ (6 \\ + 8) \\ \hline \end{array}$$

Circle the two addends that make it easier for you to add. Then find the sum.

4. $5 + 5 + 3 = \underline{\hspace{1cm}}$

5. $4 + 1 + 9 = \underline{\hspace{1cm}}$

LEARN

6. $4 + 2 + 2 = $ _____

7. $2 + 8 + 2 = $ _____

8.
$$\begin{array}{r} 8 \\ 5 \\ + 5 \\ \hline \end{array}$$

9.
$$\begin{array}{r} 9 \\ 6 \\ + 4 \\ \hline \end{array}$$

10. $6 + 3 + 1 = $ _____

11. $4 + 5 + 6 = $ _____

12. $7 + 1 + 4 = $ _____

13. $2 + 8 + 4 = $ _____

L E A R N

Grouping to Add

Three Addends

Circle the two addends you want to add first.
Add them. Then add the third addend.
Write the final sum.

1. $2 + 5 + 5 =$ _____

2. $3 + 7 + 1 =$ _____

3. $5 + 2 + 0 =$ _____

4. $3 + 4 + 6 =$ _____

5.
$$\begin{array}{r} 9 \\ 1 \\ + 1 \\ \hline \end{array}$$

6.
$$\begin{array}{r} 3 \\ 8 \\ + 2 \\ \hline \end{array}$$

TRY IT

Solve. Circle the answer.

7. $4 + 3 + 2 = ?$

    A. 6　　　　B. 7　　　　C. 9　　　　D. 13

8.

$$\begin{array}{r} 2 \\ 3 \\ +\ 1 \\ \hline \end{array}$$

    A. 4　　　　B. 5　　　　C. 6　　　　D. 10

---

9. $5 + 7 + 1 = ?$

    A. 12　　　　B. 13　　　　C. 17　　　　D. 19

10.

$$\begin{array}{r} 8 \\ 1 \\ +\ 9 \\ \hline \end{array}$$

    A. 22　　　　B. 21　　　　C. 20　　　　D. 18

TRY IT

Grouping Addends
Group Objects Different Ways

Name:

Use cubes to make the sum. For Way 1, make three trains of cubes that add to the sum. For Ways 2 and 3, connect the trains in different ways to make two trains that add to the sum. Draw the cubes.

Example: Ways to Make 10

Way 1

Way 2

Way 3

1. Ways to Make 12

Way 1

Way 2

Way 3

LEARN

2. Ways to Make 16

Way 1

Way 2	Way 3

3. Ways to Make 20

Way 1

Way 2	Way 3

Grouping Addends

Group and Regroup

Read the problem and follow the directions.

1. The circles show a total of 12 dots:

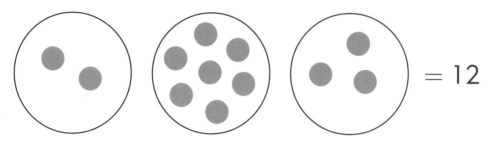

Combine two of the groups and draw dots in the circles to show a total of 12 dots in a different way:

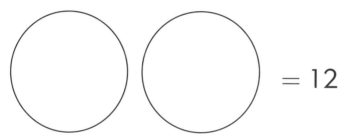

2. Draw three groups of dots to show 14:

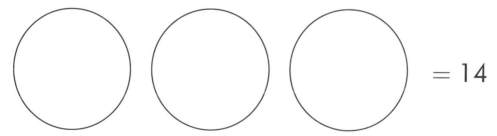

Now combine two of your groups:

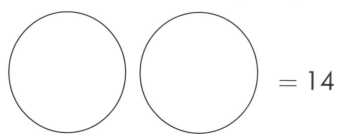

TRY IT

3. Draw three groups of dots to show 20:

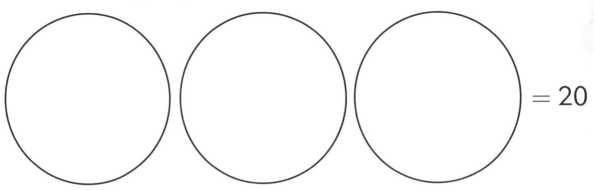 = 20

Now combine two of your groups:

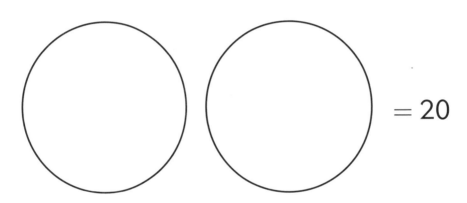 = 20

Now combine two different groups to show 20 another way:

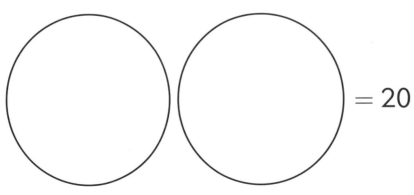 = 20

TRY IT

Grouping Addends

Sum of Three Addends

Circle the two addends you want to add first.
Add them. Then add the third addend. Write the
final sum.

1. $9 + 5 + 6 = $ _____

2. $3 + 7 + 8 = $ _____

3. $5 + 2 + 6 = $ _____

4. $10 + 2 + 5 = $ _____

5. $9 + 4 + 6 = $ _____

6. $7 + 4 + 4 = $ _____

7.
$$\begin{array}{r} 9 \\ 1 \\ + 6 \\ \hline \end{array}$$

8.
$$\begin{array}{r} 5 \\ 8 \\ + 2 \\ \hline \end{array}$$

9.
$$\begin{array}{r} 4 \\ 4 \\ + 8 \\ \hline \end{array}$$

TRY IT

Solve. Circle the answer.

10. $5 + 2 + 2 = ?$

    A. 6   B. 7   C. 9   D. 13

11.

$$\begin{array}{r} 5 \\ 0 \\ +\ 1 \\ \hline \end{array}$$

    A. 4   B. 5   C. 6   D. 10

12. $3 + 8 + 2 = ?$

    A. 12   B. 13   C. 17   D. 19

13.

$$\begin{array}{r} 9 \\ 2 \\ +\ 7 \\ \hline \end{array}$$

    A. 22   B. 21   C. 20   D. 18

TRY IT

Unit Review

Checkpoint Practice

Write the number that is 1 more than
the given number.

1. 59

2. 6

3. 63

_____   _____   _____

Write the number that is 10 more than
the given number.

4. 9

5. 20

6. 87

_____   _____   _____

Use any strategy to find the sum.

7. $23 + 5 =$ _____

8. $3 + 16 =$ _____

9. $19 + 4 =$ _____

UNIT REVIEW

Use cubes to make three groups to show the number. Then combine the groups in two different ways to find the sum. Draw all the groups.

10. 14

Find the sum. Circle the two numbers you added first. Explain your reasons for grouping those numbers.

11. $9 + 5 + 6 =$ _____   **12.** $3 + 7 + 8 =$ _____

13. $5 + 2 + 6 =$ _____

14.
$$\begin{array}{r} 9 \\ 1 \\ + \ 6 \\ \hline \end{array}$$

15.
$$\begin{array}{r} 5 \\ 8 \\ + \ 2 \\ \hline \end{array}$$

16.
$$\begin{array}{r} 4 \\ 4 \\ + \ 8 \\ \hline \end{array}$$

Circle the answer.

17. What number is 1 more than 5?

    A. 3   B. 4   C. 6   D. 11

18. What number is 1 more than 16?

    A. 15   B. 17   C. 16   D. 19

19. What number is 10 more than 35?

    A. 25   B. 36   C. 45   D. 60

20. What number is 10 more than 23?

    A. 13   B. 24   C. 33   D. 34

Use the number line to count on to find the sum. Say the answer.

21. 5 + 3

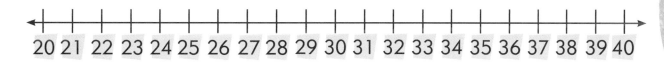

22. 22 + 11

Count on to find the sum.

23. 7 + 3 = _____   **24.** 28 + 4 = _____

Use any strategy to solve Problems 25–28.
For Problem 26, explain how you solved it.

25. $18 + 0 = ?$

    A. 18   B. 16   C. 14   D. 12

26. $9 + 6 = $ _____

27.
$$\begin{array}{r} 2 \\ 3 \\ + 1 \\ \hline \end{array}$$

    A. 4   B. 5

    C. 6   D. 10

28.
$$\begin{array}{r} 8 \\ 1 \\ + 9 \\ \hline \end{array}$$

    A. 22   B. 21

    C. 20   D. 18

29. Draw dots in the circles to show a total of 12 dots:

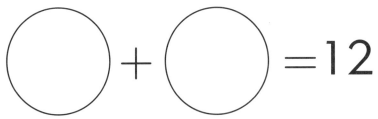

30. Now draw dots in the circles to show a total of 12 dots in a different way:

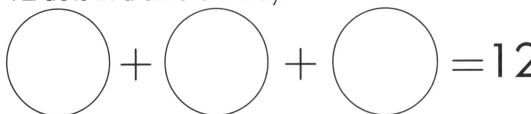

Different Forms of Numbers

Show Numbers Different Ways

Make cube trains to show the number two different ways.

1. 8

2. 10

Look at the cube train placed in front of you. Make a different train that shows the same number.

3.

4.

Draw two different pictures to show the number.

5. 8

Draw a picture to show the number represented below in a different way.

6.

TRY IT

Write two different expressions to show the number.

7. 7

Use different numbers to write an expression that shows the same number as the given expression.

8. $8 + 2$

9. $3 + 3$

Circle the answer.

10. Which shows the same number as the picture?

A.

B.

C.

D.

Use different numbers to write a number sentence that equals the same number as the number after the equals symbol.

11. $9 + 5 = 14$

12. $3 + 3 = 6$

TRY IT

Name: _____

Ways to Show Numbers

Sum It Up

Read the problem and follow the directions.

1. Draw a picture of the cube train. Write an expression that matches the train and completes the number sentence.

_____ = 15

---

2. Use cubes to make a train that matches the picture of stars. Then write an expression that completes the number sentence.

_____ = 12

---

3. Use cubes to make a train that models the expression shown. Then draw a picture to complete the number sentence.

4 + 6 + 7

_____ = 17

TRY IT

Use cubes to make two different trains to show the number two ways. Then draw pictures and write addition expressions to match each train.

4. 16

5. 13

6. 19

7. 11

Read the problem and follow the directions.

8. Draw two models for the number 13.

9. Use cubes to model the number 15 two different ways. Write the expressions for each way.

_____

_____

10. The picture uses addition to show 12. Using dots, draw another addition picture that shows 12.

TRY IT

Read the problem and follow the directions.

11. Which two pictures show 10? Circle the answer.

A. ●● + ●●●●● ●

●●● + ●●●●

B. ●●●●●● + ●●●●●

●●● + ●●●●●●●

C. ●●●●● + ●●●●●●

●●●●●●●●● + ●●●

12. Write four expressions to show the number 8.

_____   _____

_____   _____

13. $7 + 2 = 9$. Write three other expressions to show 9.

_____   _____

_____

Missing Numbers in Addition

Find Missing Numbers

Use cubes to model the number sentence.
Write the missing number.

1. $8 + 4 =$ _____

2. $8 +$ _____ $= 13$

3. $8 +$ _____ $= 14$

4. $8 +$ _____ $= 15$

5. $8 +$ _____ $= 16$

6. $8 +$ _____ $= 17$

7. $15 = 10 +$ _____

8. $15 = 9 +$ _____

9. $15 = 8 +$ _____

10. $15 = 7 +$ _____

11. $15 = 6 +$ _____

12. $15 = 5 +$ _____

L E A R N

13. ____ $+ 5 = 9$

14. $7 +$ ____ $= 12$

15. ____ $= 16 + 4$

16. $8 +$ ____ $= 17$

17. ____ $= 9 + 3$

18. ____ $+ 14 = 19$

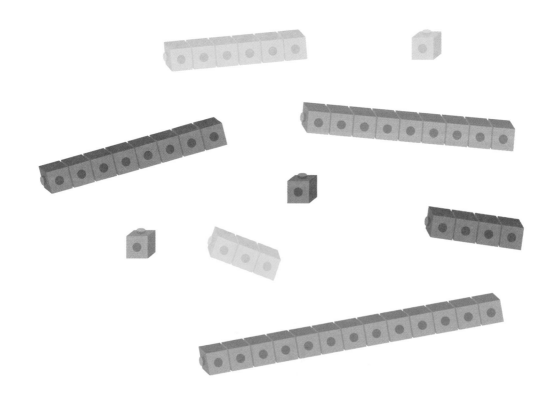

Missing Numbers in Addition

What Is Missing?

Write the missing number.

1. $7 + \underline{\hspace{1cm}} = 11$

2. $9 + \underline{\hspace{1cm}} = 13$

3. $\underline{\hspace{1cm}} + 7 = 14$

4. $12 = 8 + \underline{\hspace{1cm}}$

Circle the missing number.

5. $9 = ? + 4$

    A. 9   B. 7   C. 5   D. 3

Write the missing number.

6. $14 = 5 + \underline{\hspace{1cm}}$

TRY IT

Circle the missing number.

7. $12 = ? + 6$

    A. 18   B. 12   C. 6   D. 3

8. $13 + ? = 18$

    A. 4   B. 5   C. 8   D. 13

9. $19 = 10 + ?$

    A. 9   B. 12   C. 21   D. 27

10. $? + 9 = 12$

    A. 2   B. 3   C. 15   D. 21

Write the missing number.

11. $8 + \underline{\hspace{1cm}} = 17$

12. $\underline{\hspace{1cm}} = 2 + 7$

13. $9 + \underline{\hspace{1cm}} = 15$

14. $12 = 8 + \underline{\hspace{1cm}}$

15. $5 + \underline{\hspace{1cm}} = 12$

16. $5 + 8 = \underline{\hspace{1cm}}$

17. $\underline{\hspace{1cm}} + 6 = 14$

18. $14 = 5 + \underline{\hspace{1cm}}$

TRY IT

Circle the missing number.

19. $? + 5 = 9$

    A. 4   B. 7   C. 12   D. 14

---

20. $19 = 10 + ?$

    A. 9   B. 12   C. 21   D. 27

TRY IT

Missing Numbers in Addition Sentences

What Number Is Missing?

Write the missing number.

1. $5 + 9 = \underline{\hspace{1cm}} + 5$

2. $8 + 2 = 2 + \underline{\hspace{1cm}}$

3. $7 + \underline{\hspace{1cm}} = 10 + 7$

4. $7 + 5 = \underline{\hspace{1cm}} + 7$

5. $\underline{\hspace{1cm}} + 3 = 3 + 8$

6. $\underline{\hspace{1cm}} + 4 = 4 + 7$

7. $6 + \underline{\hspace{1cm}} = 3 + 6$

8. $6 + 9 = \underline{\hspace{1cm}} + 6$

9. $8 + 9 = 9 + \underline{\hspace{1cm}}$

10. $40 + \underline{\hspace{1cm}} = 32 + 40$

11. $67 + 45 = \underline{\hspace{1cm}} + 67$

12. $118 + 79 = 79 + \underline{\hspace{1cm}}$

TRY IT

13. $4 + 5 = \underline{\quad} + 4$

14. $5 + \underline{\quad} = 10 + 5$

15. $7 + 3 = 3 + \underline{\quad}$

16. $\underline{\quad} + 4 = 4 + 2$

17. Look at the addition sentence below.
Do you need to add to find the missing number?
Explain why or why not.

$$43 + 74 = \underline{\quad} + 43$$

Missing Numbers in Addition Sentences

Fill In the Number

Write the missing number.

1. $2 + 10 = \underline{\hspace{1cm}} + 2$

2. $8 + 3 = 3 + \underline{\hspace{1cm}}$

3. $1 + \underline{\hspace{1cm}} = 6 + 1$

4. $8 + 9 = \underline{\hspace{1cm}} + 8$

5. $\underline{\hspace{1cm}} + 6 = 6 + 4$

6. $\underline{\hspace{1cm}} + 2 = 2 + 7$

7. $7 + \underline{\hspace{1cm}} = 3 + 7$

8. $10 + 9 = \underline{\hspace{1cm}} + 10$

9. $9 + 3 = 3 + \underline{\hspace{1cm}}$

10. $9 + 8 = \underline{\hspace{1cm}} + 9$

11. $45 + \underline{\hspace{1cm}} = 112 + 45$

12. $23 + 54 = \underline{\hspace{1cm}} + 23$

13. $167 + 70 = 70 + \underline{\hspace{1cm}}$

TRY IT

14. Look at the addition sentence below. Do you need to add the numbers to find the missing number? Explain why or why not.

$$66 + 113 = 113 + \underline{\qquad}$$

Circle the missing number.

15. $6 + 6 = ? + 6$

    A. 18   B. 12   C. 6   D. 3

16. $8 + 5 = ? + 8$

    A. 5   B. 8   C. 13   D. 3

17. $2 + 9 = ? + 9$

    A. 11   B. 9   C. 7   D. 2

Write the missing numbers.

18. $20 + 40 = \underline{\qquad} + \underline{\qquad} + 40$

Make cube trains to show the number two different ways.

1. 7

2. 9

3. Draw two different pictures to show 10.

Write two expressions to show the number.

4. 8

5. 6

6. Use cubes to show 14 two ways. Then draw pictures and write addition expressions to match each train.

Write the missing number for the addition sentence.

7. ____ $+ 4 = 12$	**8.** $6 +$ ____ $= 15$
9. $8 + 9 =$ ____ $+ 8$	**10.** $8 +$ ____ $= 3 + 8$
11. ____ $+ 8 = 15$	**12.** $5 + 9 =$ ____ $+ 7$
13. $25 =$ ____ $+ 5$	**14.** ____ $= 9 + 3$

Read the problem and follow the directions.

15. Use the cubes to model the number 17 two different ways. Use more than one group of cubes for at least one of your models.

16. Draw two pictures to show the number 20.

17. Which answer choice shows the same number as the picture below? Circle the answer.
$7 = ☺☺ + ☺☺☺☺☺$

A. $7 = ●●●● + ●●●●$

B. $7 = ●●●●●●●$

C. $7 = ●●●●●● + ●●●$

D. $7 = ●●●●●● + ●$

Understand Subtraction

Show Subtraction

Say the answer.

1. What does it mean to subtract 6 books from a stack of 13 books?

2. What does it mean to subtract 5 balls from a pile of 10 balls?

3. What does it mean to subtract 3 marbles from a pile of 7 marbles?

4. What does the drawing show?

**Use blocks to model the problem.
Then write the answer.**

5. 10 take away 3

_____

6. 10 take away 7

_____

7. 5 subtracted from 12

_____

8. 3 subtracted from 8

_____

9. Pam has 5 balls.
She gives away 2 balls.
How many balls does
Pam have left?

_____

10. Ray has 9 blocks.
He gives 4 to his sister.
How many blocks does
Ray have left?

_____

Draw a picture to model the problem. Then write the answer.

11. 6 subtracted from 11. _____

12. 11 take away 3. _____

13. There are 11 heart stickers.
Tina uses 4 of them.

How many stickers are left? _____

14. Adam has 6 stamps.
He uses 4 stamps.

How many stamps does he have left? _____

Circle the answer.

15. Jenny has 10 crackers. If you take away 8 crackers, Jenny has 2 crackers left. Which explains this problem?

    A. Two numbers were added together.

    B. One number was subtracted from another number.

    C. Two numbers were compared to see which was greater.

16. Which picture shows 4 subtracted from 12?

    A.

    B.

    C.

    D.

TRY IT

The Minus Symbol

Write the Subtraction

Say the answer.

1. What is this symbol?

What does — mean?

2. What does

$9 - 6$ mean?

Use numbers, the minus symbol, and the equals symbol to write a number sentence for the picture.

3.

_____

4.

_____

Draw a picture with dots to show the expression.

5. $9 - 1$ **6.** $8 - 2$

TRY IT

Circle the answer.

7. Which number sentence shows that nine minus six equals three?

A. $3 + 6 = 9$ B. $6 - 3 = 3$ C. $9 - 6 = 3$

8. Which model shows 14 dots take away 12 dots is 2 dots?

A. ● ● ✖ ✖ ✖ ✖ ✖ ✖ ✖ ✖ ✖ ✖ ✖ ✖

B. ● ● ● ● ✖ ✖ ✖ ✖ ✖ ✖ ✖ ✖ ✖

C. ● ● ✖ ✖ ✖ ✖ ✖ ✖ ✖ ✖ ✖ ✖

9. Sammy has 6 pieces of candy. He takes away 2 and has 4 left. Which model shows this problem?

A. 🍬 ✖ ✖ ✖ ✖ ✖

B. 🍬 🍬 🍬 🍬 ✖ ✖

C. 🍬 🍬 🍬 ✖ ✖ ✖

10. What does the — symbol mean in this number sentence? $13 = 20 - 7$

A. plus

B. equals

C. minus

TRY IT

Equal Expressions

Subtraction and the Equals Symbol

Tell what the $=$ symbol means in the number sentences.

1. $8 - 4 = 4$

2. $6 = 6 - 0$

3. $7 = 13 - 6$

4. $3 = 8 - 5$

Write the missing symbol.

5. $12 - 4 \boxed{} 8$

6. $3 = 11 \boxed{} 8$

7. $6 - 2 \boxed{} 7 - 3$

Tell whether the equals symbol or not-equal-to symbol belongs between the cards.

8. $\boxed{5 - 2}$ $\boxed{3}$

9. $\boxed{6}$ $\boxed{11 - 5}$

10. $\boxed{10 - 6}$ $\boxed{3}$

TRY IT

Circle the answer.

11. John writes $4 + 2$ on the left-hand side of a paper and then writes $7 - 1$ to the right of it.
Which is the correct symbol to write between the two sets of numbers?

A. $+$ B. $-$ C. $=$ D. $\neq$

12. Elisa writes $7 - 2$ on the left-hand side of a paper and then writes 4 to the right of it.
Which is the correct symbol to write between the two sets of numbers?

A. $+$ B. $-$ C. $\neq$ D. $=$

13. What does the symbol the arrow is pointing to mean?

$$11 - 7 \overset{\downarrow}{=} 4$$

A. equals   B. not equal to

C. add   D. subtract

Circle the missing symbol.

14. $4 \; \boxed{} \; 10 - 6$

A. $+$ B. $-$ C. $=$ D. $\neq$

15. $5 - 1 \; \boxed{} \; 8 - 4$

A. $+$ B. $-$ C. $=$ D. $\neq$

T R Y   I T

Put Together, Take Away

Show Subtraction

Use cubes for Problems 1–5. Read each problem, make the model, and answer the questions.

1. Add 10 red cubes and 4 yellow cubes.
    Subtract 4 yellow cubes.

    How many cubes are left? _____

2. Subtract 3 cubes from 7 cubes.
    Add 3 cubes.

    How many cubes are there? _____

3. Add 7 cubes to 9 cubes.

    What is the total? _____

    How do you get 9 cubes again as the total?

4. Subtract 5 cubes from 12 cubes.

    How many cubes are left? _____

    How do you get 12 cubes again as the total?

5. Johnny added 9 to a number. Then he subtracted 9 from the total.

    What number was left? Use cubes to explain.

TRY IT

Answer the questions.

6.

   How many cubes are there altogether? _____

   If you subtract the yellow cubes,
   how many cubes will you have left? _____

7. How many cubes are there altogether? _____

   If you subtract the orange cubes,
   how many cubes will you have left? _____

8. How many cubes are there altogether? _____

   If you subtract the yellow cubes,
   how many cubes will you have left? _____

9. Add the circles and the squares.
   How many are there in all? _____

   Draw an X over all the circles.
   How many squares are left? _____

TRY IT

Order and Zero in Subtraction

Subtraction Rules

Use circles to model the problem. Decide which symbol is correct. Circle the answer.

1. $8 - 6 \;\genfrac{}{}{0pt}{}{=}{\neq}\; 6 - 8$

2. $12 - 7 \;\genfrac{}{}{0pt}{}{=}{\neq}\; 7 - 12$

3. $14 - 9 \;\genfrac{}{}{0pt}{}{=}{\neq}\; 9 - 14$

4. $5 - 1 \;\genfrac{}{}{0pt}{}{=}{\neq}\; 1 - 5$

Follow the directions and say the answer.

5. Ken uses circles to model $7 - 2$. After taking away 2 circles, he has 5 circles left. So the difference is 5. If you use circles to model $2 - 7$, will you get the same answer? Explain why or why not.

6. Is $6 - 1$ the same as $1 - 6$? Use circles to explain why or why not.

7. Use circles to model $6 - 4$. If you change the order of the numbers to $4 - 6$, will you get the same answer?

8. Simone has a set of 9 cards. She gives away 6 cards and has 3 left. If she started with 6 cards, could she give away 9 and still have 3 left? Explain why or why not.

TRY IT

9. Use circles to show that $8 - 3$ is not the same as $3 - 8$.

10. Jack has a set of 7 pens. He gives away 3 pens and has 4 left. If he started with 3 pens, could he give away 7 and still have 4 left? Explain why or why not.

Write the answer.

11. $8 - 0 =$ _____

12. $18 - 0 =$ _____

13. $79 - 0 =$ _____

14. $318 - 0 =$ _____

15. Mark had 12 stickers. He gave away zero stickers. How many stickers does Mark have left?

_____ stickers

16. What happens to a number when you subtract zero from it?

_____

_____

17. When you subtract 0 from 11, how many are left?

_____

18. What number goes in the box?

$$14 - \boxed{} = 14$$

Subtract to Compare

How Many Greater or Less?

Model the problem using cubes and grid paper.
Then write the answer.

1. How many greater is 3 than 2? _____

2. How many more is 8 than 6? _____

3. How many less than 20 is 10? _____

4. How many less than 9 is 1? _____

5. $10 - 5 =$ _____

6. $5 - 2 =$ _____

7. $10 - 6 =$ _____

8. $8 - 0 =$ _____

Make a drawing to model the problem.
Then write the answer.

9. How many greater is 20 than 15? _____

10. How many less than 10 is 4? _____

T R Y   I T

11. 3 subtracted from 12 _____

12. 11 take away 5 _____

13. $4 - 2 =$ _____

14. $7 - 6 =$ _____

15. Jenny has 6 stickers. George has 4 stickers. How many fewer stickers does George have than Jenny?

_____ stickers

TRY IT

Use Pairs to Subtract

Line Up to Subtract

Draw lines to make pairs between rows. Then circle the objects left over to solve. Write the answers.

1. How many greater is 8 than 6? _____

$8 - 6 =$ _____

2. How many less is 7 than 12? _____

$12 - 7 =$ _____

3. How many greater is 6 than 2? _____

$6 - 2 =$ _____

TRY IT

4. How many greater is 10 than 5? _____

$10 - 5 =$ _____

5. How many less is 5 than 9? _____

$9 - 5 =$ _____

Draw your own picture to solve the problem.

6. How many less is 3 than 6? _____

$6 - 3 =$ _____

Use Pairs to Subtract

Sketch Objects to Subtract

Model the problem using cubes and grid paper.
Then write the answer.

1. How many greater is 9 than 8? _____

2. How many greater is 13 than 10? _____

3. How many less is 6 than 8? _____

4. How many less is 9 than 15? _____

5. How many greater is 11 than 9? _____

6. 14 is how many less than 20? _____

7. 9 take away 2 _____

8. 8 take away 5 _____

9. $18 - 6$ _____

10. $7 - 4$ _____

11. $4 - 2 =$ _____

12. $12 - 8 =$ _____

13. $8 - 3 =$ _____

TRY IT

Make a drawing to model the problem.
Then write the answer.

14. $7 - 6 = $ ____

15. $10 - 3 = $ ____

16. $9 - 4 = $ ____

17. $10 - 4 = $ ____

18. Noelle has 7 books and Georgia has 3 books. Draw a picture to show how many fewer books Georgia has than Noelle.

____ books

T R Y I T

Unit Review

Checkpoint Practice

Draw a picture to show the subtraction.
Write the answer.

1. Nick has 10 marbles.
He gives 4 to his brother.
How many marbles does Nick have left?

_____ marbles

Write a subtraction number sentence to match
the picture or words.

2.

_____

3. 12 take away 6 is 6

_____

Write the missing symbol.

4. $7 - 5 \boxed{} 2$

5. $11 \boxed{} 5 = 6$

UNIT REVIEW

Write = if the expressions are equal.
Write ≠ if the expressions are not equal.

6. 6 − 2 ☐ 4

7. 8 ☐ 12 − 3

8. 3 − 1 ☐ 4 − 2

9. 9 − 4 ☐ 4 − 9

Use circle blocks to model the problem. Write the answer.

10. Add 8 circles to 6 circles.
What is the total?   _____

What do you have to do to get back to 8 circles?

11. Curtis added 5 to a number.
Then he subtracted 5 from the total.

What number was left?   _____

12. Jenny had 15 photos.
She gave away 0 photos.

How many photos does Jenny have left?   _____

Use circle blocks and grid paper to model the
problem. Write the answer.

13. How many greater is 10 than 7?   _____

14. How many less is 6 than 7?   _____

Circle the answer.

15. Tom did not know what to do when he saw the — symbol in the following problem. $8 - 3 = ?$

What would you tell Tom to do?

A. Add the numbers.

B. Group the numbers.

C. Subtract the numbers.

16. Which model shows 10 take away 5 equals 5?

A.

B.

C.

17. Amy writes $5 + 3$ on the left-hand side of a paper and then writes $10 - 2$ to the right of it. Which is the correct symbol to write between the two sets of numbers?

A. $=$ B. $+$ C. $\neq$

Write the correct symbol or number in the box to make the number sentence true.

18. $7 \boxed{} 4 = 3$ **19.** $21 - \boxed{} = 21$

Tell what the equals symbol means in the number sentence.

20. $3 - 1 = 2$

21. $5 = 7 - 2$

Use circle blocks to model the problem. Write the answer.

22. Show 6 take away 2, and write the answer. _____

23. Show how to add 11 and 9. How many circles in all? _____

Now take away 9 from this group of circles. How many are left? _____

24. Show how to subtract $5 - 4$. If you try to subtract $4 - 5$, will you get the same answer? Explain why or why not.

Draw a picture to show how to solve the problem. Write the answer.

25. How much greater is 16 than 8? _____

Subtraction Facts Through 8

Practice Facts

Use circles to model the problem.
Then write the answer.

1. $7 - 4 = $ _____   **2.** $6 - 1 = $ _____

3. $5 - 4 = $ _____   **4.** $4 - 4 = $ _____

5. $8 - 4 = $ _____   **6.** $3 - 2 = $ _____

7. $8 - 2 = $ _____   **8.** $7 - 5 = $ _____

9. $8 - 6 = $ _____   **10.** $7 - 2 = $ _____

11. $6 - 4 = $ _____   **12.** $5 - 3 = $ _____

T R Y   I T

Use an addition fact to solve. Then write the answer.

13. $6 - 3 =$ _____

14. $5 - 3 =$ _____

15. $4 - 3 =$ _____

16. $3 - 3 =$ _____

Use any strategy to solve. Then write the answer.

17. $3 - 2 =$ _____

18. $5 - 2 =$ _____

19. $7 - 3 =$ _____

20. $6 - 4 =$ _____

21. $8 - 1 =$ _____

22. $2 - 1 =$ _____

23. $8 - 5 =$ _____

24. $4 - 2 =$ _____

25. $7 - 4 =$ _____

26. $6 - 2 =$ _____

27.
$$\begin{array}{r} 7 \\ -\ 2 \\ \hline \end{array}$$

28.
$$\begin{array}{r} 7 \\ -\ 1 \\ \hline \end{array}$$

29.
$$\begin{array}{r} 8 \\ -\ 6 \\ \hline \end{array}$$

30.
$$\begin{array}{r} 8 \\ -\ 5 \\ \hline \end{array}$$

Circle the answer.

31. $4 - 2 = ?$

A. 5   B. 2

C. 1   D. 0

32. $3 - 1 = ?$

A. 0   B. 1

C. 2   D. 3

TRY IT

Relate Addition and Subtraction

Subtraction Facts

Complete the fact family.

1. 2, 5, 7

$2 + 5 = 7$

$7 - 5 = 2$

___ + ___ = ___

___ − ___ = ___

2. 1, 3, 4

$1 + 3 = 4$

$4 - 3 = 1$

___ + ___ = ___

___ − ___ = ___

3. 6, 2, 8

___ + ___ = ___

___ + ___ = ___

___ − ___ = ___

___ − ___ = ___

4. 2, 2, 4

___ + ___ = ___

___ − ___ = ___

TRY IT

Solve the addition facts for the subtraction sentence. Then find the difference.

5. $8 - 5 = ?$

$5 + \underline{} = 8$

$\underline{} + 5 = 8$

$8 - 5 = \underline{}$

6. $5 - 0 = ?$

$0 + \underline{} = 5$

$\underline{} + 0 = 5$

$5 - 0 = \underline{}$

7. $6 - 4 = ?$

$4 + \underline{} = 6$

$\underline{} + 4 = 6$

$6 - 4 = \underline{}$

8. $7 - 1 = ?$

$1 + \underline{} = 7$

$\underline{} + 1 = 7$

$7 - 1 = \underline{}$

9. Place 6 red cubes in a group and 2 blue cubes in a separate group. How many cubes are there in all? If you take away the blue cubes, how many cubes will be left?

Write the difference. Explain how you found the answer.

10. $8 - 5 =$ _____

11. $5 - 0 =$ _____

12. $8 - 3 =$ _____

13. $7 - 0 =$ _____

14.
$$\begin{array}{r} 8 \\ -\ 4 \\ \hline \end{array}$$

15.
$$\begin{array}{r} 7 \\ -\ 1 \\ \hline \end{array}$$

16.
$$\begin{array}{r} 3 \\ -\ 3 \\ \hline \end{array}$$

17.
$$\begin{array}{r} 6 \\ -\ 4 \\ \hline \end{array}$$

T R Y I T

Circle the answer.

18. $6 - 0 = ?$

    A. 6   B. 5   C. 8

Write the difference.

19. $7 - 3 =$ ____   **20.** $6 - 4 =$ ____

21. $7 - 4 =$ ____   **22.** $3 - 2 =$ ____

23.
$$\begin{array}{r} 8 \\ -\ 3 \\ \hline \end{array}$$

24.
$$\begin{array}{r} 7 \\ -\ 5 \\ \hline \end{array}$$

25.
$$\begin{array}{r} 8 \\ -\ 1 \\ \hline \end{array}$$

TRY IT

Subtraction Facts Through 12

Subtraction Patterns

Look for a pattern or use cubes to find each difference.

1. $9 - 0 =$ _____

$9 - 1 =$ _____

$9 - 2 =$ _____

$9 - 3 =$ _____

$9 - 4 =$ _____

$9 - 5 =$ _____

$9 - 6 =$ _____

$9 - 7 =$ _____

$9 - 8 =$ _____

$9 - 9 =$ _____

2. $10 - 0 =$ _____

$10 - 1 =$ _____

$10 - 2 =$ _____

$10 - 3 =$ _____

$10 - 4 =$ _____

$10 - 5 =$ _____

$10 - 6 =$ _____

$10 - 7 =$ _____

$10 - 8 =$ _____

$10 - 9 =$ _____

$10 - 10 =$ _____

LEARN

3. $11 - 1 =$ ____

$11 - 2 =$ ____

$11 - 3 =$ ____

$11 - 4 =$ ____

$11 - 5 =$ ____

$11 - 6 =$ ____

$11 - 7 =$ ____

$11 - 8 =$ ____

$11 - 9 =$ ____

$11 - 10 =$ ____

4. $12 - 2 =$ ____

$12 - 3 =$ ____

$12 - 4 =$ ____

$12 - 5 =$ ____

$12 - 6 =$ ____

$12 - 7 =$ ____

$12 - 8 =$ ____

$12 - 9 =$ ____

$12 - 10 =$ ____

L E A R N

Subtraction Facts Through 12

Let's Subtract

Write the difference. Describe any patterns you see.

1. $\begin{array}{r} 5 \\ -\ 5 \\ \hline \end{array}$

2. $\begin{array}{r} 5 \\ -\ 4 \\ \hline \end{array}$

3. $\begin{array}{r} 5 \\ -\ 3 \\ \hline \end{array}$

4. $\begin{array}{r} 5 \\ -\ 2 \\ \hline \end{array}$

5. $\begin{array}{r} 9 \\ -\ 7 \\ \hline \end{array}$

6. $\begin{array}{r} 9 \\ -\ 6 \\ \hline \end{array}$

7. $\begin{array}{r} 9 \\ -\ 5 \\ \hline \end{array}$

8. $\begin{array}{r} 9 \\ -\ 4 \\ \hline \end{array}$

9. $\begin{array}{r} 7 \\ -\ 4 \\ \hline \end{array}$

10. $\begin{array}{r} 6 \\ -\ 4 \\ \hline \end{array}$

11. $\begin{array}{r} 5 \\ -\ 4 \\ \hline \end{array}$

12. $\begin{array}{r} 4 \\ -\ 4 \\ \hline \end{array}$

13. $\begin{array}{r} 12 \\ -\ 6 \\ \hline \end{array}$

14. $\begin{array}{r} 12 \\ -\ 7 \\ \hline \end{array}$

15. $\begin{array}{r} 12 \\ -\ 8 \\ \hline \end{array}$

16. $\begin{array}{r} 12 \\ -\ 9 \\ \hline \end{array}$

LEARN

17.   8
      − 8

18.   8
      − 7

19.   8
      − 6

20.   8
      − 3

21.   11
      − 9

22.   11
      − 8

23.   11
      − 7

24.   11
      − 6

25.   12
      − 4

26.   12
      − 5

27.   12
      − 6

28.   12
      −7

29.   8
      − 2

30.   10
      − 4

31.   9
      − 5

32.   12
      − 5

LEARN

Subtraction Facts Through 12

Find the Difference

Write the difference.

1. 11
    − 9

2. 11
    − 8

3. 11
    − 7

4. 11
    − 6

5. 12
    − 7

6. 12
    − 6

7. 12
    − 5

8. 12
    − 4

9. 8
    − 3

10. 7
    − 3

11. 6
    − 3

12. 5
    − 3

13. 7
    − 1

14. 7
    − 2

TRY IT

15. 7
  − 3

16. 7
  − 4

17. 12
  − 5

18. 4
  − 3

19. 11
  − 7

20. 7
  − 5

21. 11
  − 4

22. 11
  − 5

23. 10
  − 5

24. 10
  − 3

25. 12
  − 8

26. 12
  − 9

Circle the answer.

27. $12 - 3 = ?$

    A. 9

    B. 8

    C. 10

28. $11 - 2 = ?$

    A. 9

    B. 7

    C. 8

TRY IT

Count Back Subtraction Facts

Subtract, Subtract

Part 1: Write the difference.

1. $5 - 2 =$ _____

2. $12 - 2 =$ _____

3. $9 - 1 =$ _____

4. $11 - 1 =$ _____

5. $7 - 4 =$ _____

6. $11 - 9 =$ _____

7. $\begin{array}{r} 9 \\ -\ 0 \\ \hline \end{array}$

8. $\begin{array}{r} 8 \\ -\ 5 \\ \hline \end{array}$

9. $\begin{array}{r} 12 \\ -\ 6 \\ \hline \end{array}$

10. $\begin{array}{r} 10 \\ -\ 6 \\ \hline \end{array}$

11. $\begin{array}{r} 11 \\ -\ 5 \\ \hline \end{array}$

12. $\begin{array}{r} 6 \\ -\ 3 \\ \hline \end{array}$

13. $11 - 7 =$ _____

14. $9 - 8 =$ _____

15. $11 - 4 =$ _____

TRY IT

Part 2: Write the difference.

1. $10 - 5 =$ _____

2. $11 - 9 =$ _____

3. $9 - 9 =$ _____

4. $11 - 5 =$ _____

5. $9 - 4 =$ _____

6. $12 - 3 =$ _____

7. $11 - 6 =$ _____

8. $9 - 5 =$ _____

9. $12 - 7 =$ _____

10. $11 - 7 =$ _____

11. $\begin{array}{r} 12 \\ -\ 6 \\ \hline \end{array}$

12. $\begin{array}{r} 10 \\ -\ 4 \\ \hline \end{array}$

13. $\begin{array}{r} 11 \\ -\ 1 \\ \hline \end{array}$

14. $\begin{array}{r} 12 \\ -\ 4 \\ \hline \end{array}$

15. $\begin{array}{r} 10 \\ -\ 9 \\ \hline \end{array}$

16. $\begin{array}{r} 12 \\ -\ 2 \\ \hline \end{array}$

17. $\begin{array}{r} 10 \\ -\ 7 \\ \hline \end{array}$

18. $\begin{array}{r} 12 \\ -\ 7 \\ \hline \end{array}$

19. $12 - 9 =$ _____

20. $11 - 7 =$ _____

21. $10 - 4 =$ _____

Subtraction Facts Through 16

Color Facts

These subtraction problems have answers of
4, 6, 7, or 8. Find each difference. Color each space:
4 – green, 6 – red, 7 – blue, 8 – yellow.

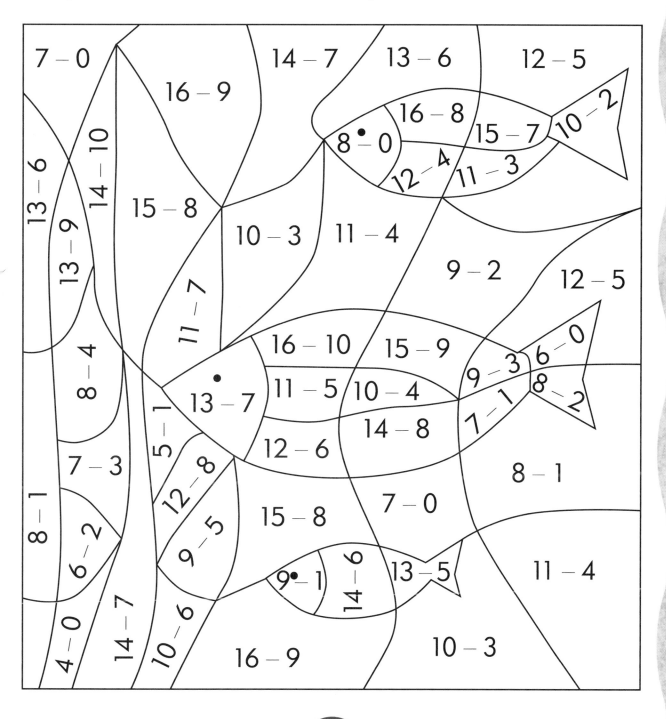

L E A R N

Subtraction Facts Through 16

Practice Subtraction Facts

Write the difference.

1. $15 - 8 =$ _____

2. $1 - 0 =$ _____

3. $16 - 8 =$ _____

4. $14 - 5 =$ _____

5. $16 - 9 =$ _____

6. $11 - 10 =$ _____

7. $15 - 7 =$ _____

8. $13 - 4 =$ _____

9. $10 - 9 =$ _____

10.
$$\begin{array}{r} 8 \\ -5 \\ \hline \end{array}$$

11.
$$\begin{array}{r} 13 \\ -6 \\ \hline \end{array}$$

12.
$$\begin{array}{r} 15 \\ -9 \\ \hline \end{array}$$

13.
$$\begin{array}{r} 9 \\ -7 \\ \hline \end{array}$$

14.
$$\begin{array}{r} 13 \\ -8 \\ \hline \end{array}$$

15.
$$\begin{array}{r} 15 \\ -6 \\ \hline \end{array}$$

TRY IT

16. $15 - 5 =$ _____

17. $16 - 9 =$ _____

18. $7 - 3 =$ _____

19. $14 - 4 =$ _____

20. $\begin{array}{r} 16 \\ -\ 9 \\ \hline \end{array}$

21. $\begin{array}{r} 11 \\ -\ 2 \\ \hline \end{array}$

22. $\begin{array}{r} 13 \\ -\ 7 \\ \hline \end{array}$

23. $\begin{array}{r} 9 \\ -\ 3 \\ \hline \end{array}$

Circle the answer.

24. $14 - 7 = ?$

A. 7

B. 6

C. 5

D. 4

25. $11 - 6 = ?$

A. 7

B. 6

C. 5

D. 4

TRY IT

Facts Using Subtraction

Know Subtraction Facts

Part 1: Write the difference.

1.   14
        − 7

2.   9
        − 5

3.   16
        − 6

4.   13
        − 5

5.   7
        − 0

6.   14
        − 5

7.   16
        − 6

8.   15
        − 6

9. $13 - 7 =$ _____

10. $5 - 5 =$ _____

11.   13
        − 10

12.   16
        − 7

Circle the answer.

13. $13 - 9 = ?$

A. 3   B. 4

C. 5   D. 6

14. $14 - 5 = ?$

A. 5   B. 7

C. 9   D. 10

TRY IT

Part 2: Write the difference.

1. $16 - 6 = \underline{}$

2. $14 - 6 = \underline{}$

3. $13 - 7 = \underline{}$

4. $14 - 8 = \underline{}$

5. $14 - 7 = \underline{}$

6. $16 - 10 = \underline{}$

7. $15 - 6 = \underline{}$

8. $14 - 4 = \underline{}$

9.
$$\begin{array}{r} 15 \\ -\ 8 \\ \hline \end{array}$$

10.
$$\begin{array}{r} 13 \\ -\ 6 \\ \hline \end{array}$$

11.
$$\begin{array}{r} 16 \\ -\ 10 \\ \hline \end{array}$$

12.
$$\begin{array}{r} 13 \\ -\ 8 \\ \hline \end{array}$$

13.
$$\begin{array}{r} 13 \\ -\ 5 \\ \hline \end{array}$$

14.
$$\begin{array}{r} 15 \\ -\ 7 \\ \hline \end{array}$$

15.
$$\begin{array}{r} 16 \\ -\ 8 \\ \hline \end{array}$$

16.
$$\begin{array}{r} 13 \\ -\ 3 \\ \hline \end{array}$$

17. $13 - 4 = \underline{}$

18. $14 - 7 = \underline{}$

19. $13 - 6 = \underline{}$

20. $16 - 8 = \underline{}$

TRY IT

Subtraction Through 20

Choose a Strategy

Name:

Write the difference. Tell what strategy you used.

1. 9
  − 3

2. 11
  − 1

3. 12
  − 6

4. 7
  − 1

5. 16 − 8 = _____

6. 15 − 5 = _____

7. 13 − 9 = _____

8. 18 − 10 = _____

9. 12 − 5 = _____

10. 13 − 6 = _____

11. 17 − 8 = _____

12. 5 − 4 = _____

13. 11
  − 3

14. 13
  − 8

15. 14
  − 8

16. 17
  − 8

LEARN

17.   16
       − 7

18.   15
       − 6

19.   7
       − 5

20.   9
       − 8

21. 16 − 8 = _____

22. 15 − 5 = _____

23.   17
       − 9

24.   11
       − 8

25.   14
       − 7

26.   10
       − 8

27.   8
       − 2

28.   15
       − 7

29.   17
       − 8

30.   16
       − 8

L E A R N

Subtraction Through 20

All the Facts

Write the difference.

1. 9
− 2

2. 6
− 1

3. 12
− 2

4. 5
− 1

5. 15
− 2

6. 15
− 7

7. 15
− 6

8. 15
− 5

9. 11 − 8 = _____

10. 13 − 5 = _____

11. 17 − 8 = _____

12. 20 − 10 = _____

Circle the answer.

13. $16 - 8 = ?$

    A. 7   B. 8

    C. 9   D. 10

14. $16 - 7 = ?$

    A. 9   B. 7

    C. 6   D. 4

15. $15 - 9 = ?$

    A. 10   B. 8

    C. 6   D. 4

16. $15 - 6 = ?$

    A. 6   B. 7

    C. 8   D. 9

Write the difference.

17.
$$\begin{array}{r} 17 \\ -\ 9 \\ \hline \end{array}$$

18.
$$\begin{array}{r} 17 \\ -\ 8 \\ \hline \end{array}$$

19.
$$\begin{array}{r} 19 \\ -\ 9 \\ \hline \end{array}$$

20.
$$\begin{array}{r} 16 \\ -\ 10 \\ \hline \end{array}$$

21.
$$\begin{array}{r} 20 \\ -\ 10 \\ \hline \end{array}$$

22.
$$\begin{array}{r} 18 \\ -\ 9 \\ \hline \end{array}$$

23.
$$\begin{array}{r} 16 \\ -\ 8 \\ \hline \end{array}$$

24.
$$\begin{array}{r} 17 \\ -\ 10 \\ \hline \end{array}$$

25. $14 - 7 = $ _____

26. $18 - 8 = $ _____

27. $16 - 9 = $ _____

28. $16 - 8 = $ _____

TRY IT

All the Subtraction Facts

Subtract the Facts

Part 1: Write the difference.

1. $20 - 10 = $ _____

2. $5 - 5 = $ _____

3. $10 - 1 = $ _____

4. $13 - 7 = $ _____

5. $\begin{array}{r} 18 \\ -\ 8 \\ \hline \end{array}$

6. $\begin{array}{r} 15 \\ -\ 7 \\ \hline \end{array}$

7. $\begin{array}{r} 16 \\ -\ 8 \\ \hline \end{array}$

8. $\begin{array}{r} 14 \\ -\ 5 \\ \hline \end{array}$

9. $\begin{array}{r} 16 \\ -\ 9 \\ \hline \end{array}$

10. $\begin{array}{r} 17 \\ -\ 9 \\ \hline \end{array}$

11. $\begin{array}{r} 7 \\ -\ 0 \\ \hline \end{array}$

12. $\begin{array}{r} 19 \\ -\ 10 \\ \hline \end{array}$

13. $\begin{array}{r} 20 \\ -\ 10 \\ \hline \end{array}$

14. $\begin{array}{r} 19 \\ -\ 9 \\ \hline \end{array}$

15. $\begin{array}{r} 12 \\ -\ 9 \\ \hline \end{array}$

16. $\begin{array}{r} 17 \\ -\ 8 \\ \hline \end{array}$

TRY IT

Part 2: Write the difference.

1. $\begin{array}{r} 16 \\ -9 \\ \hline \end{array}$ **2.** $\begin{array}{r} 20 \\ -10 \\ \hline \end{array}$ **3.** $\begin{array}{r} 17 \\ -8 \\ \hline \end{array}$ **4.** $\begin{array}{r} 19 \\ -9 \\ \hline \end{array}$

5. $16 - 8 =$ _____   **6.** $15 - 9 =$ _____

7. $16 - 6 =$ _____   **8.** $15 - 10 =$ _____

9. $\begin{array}{r} 18 \\ -10 \\ \hline \end{array}$ **10.** $\begin{array}{r} 17 \\ -9 \\ \hline \end{array}$ **11.** $\begin{array}{r} 19 \\ -8 \\ \hline \end{array}$ **12.** $\begin{array}{r} 16 \\ -10 \\ \hline \end{array}$

13. $\begin{array}{r} 12 \\ -2 \\ \hline \end{array}$ **14.** $\begin{array}{r} 19 \\ -10 \\ \hline \end{array}$ **15.** $\begin{array}{r} 17 \\ -10 \\ \hline \end{array}$ **16.** $\begin{array}{r} 15 \\ -8 \\ \hline \end{array}$

17. $\begin{array}{r} 15 \\ -9 \\ \hline \end{array}$ **18.** $\begin{array}{r} 15 \\ -5 \\ \hline \end{array}$ **19.** $\begin{array}{r} 18 \\ -9 \\ \hline \end{array}$ **20.** $\begin{array}{r} 17 \\ -7 \\ \hline \end{array}$

TRY IT

Unit Review

Checkpoint Practice

Part 1: Untimed
Complete the fact family.

1. 4, 3, 7

___ + ___ = ___

___ + ___ = ___

___ − ___ = ___

___ − ___ = ___

2. 3, 3, 6

___ + ___ = ___

___ − ___ = ___

Solve the addition facts for each subtraction sentence. Then find the difference.

3. $6 - 2 = ?$

$2 + $ ___ $= 6$

___ $+ 2 = 6$

$6 - 2 = $ ___

4. $8 - 0 = ?$

$0 + $ ___ $= 8$

___ $+ 0 = 8$

$8 - 0 = $ ___

Write the difference.

5. $9 - 2 = $ ___

6. $11 - 6 = $ ___

7. $9 - 5 = $ ___

8. $6 - 0 = $ ___

9. $13 - 5 =$ _____

10. $20 - 10 =$ _____

11. $14 - 5 =$ _____

12. $15 - 7 =$ _____

13.
$$\begin{array}{r} 15 \\ -\ 10 \\ \hline \end{array}$$

14.
$$\begin{array}{r} 18 \\ -\ 8 \\ \hline \end{array}$$

15.
$$\begin{array}{r} 16 \\ -\ 7 \\ \hline \end{array}$$

16.
$$\begin{array}{r} 18 \\ -\ 9 \\ \hline \end{array}$$

For Problems 17–19, place 8 red circles in a group. Then place 4 green circles in a separate group.

17. How would you add together the green and red circles?

18. How many red and green circles are there in all? _____

19. If you remove the 4 green circles, how many circles will be left? _____

For Problems 20–22, place 7 red circles in a group. Then place 2 green circles in a separate group.

20. How would you add together the green and red circles?

21. How many circles are there in all? ____

22. If you take away the green circles, how many circles will be left? ____

Write the difference.

23. $7 - 2 =$ ____

24. $6 - 6 =$ ____

25. $11 - 2 =$ ____

26. $9 - 6 =$ ____

27.
$$\begin{array}{r} 12 \\ -\ 8 \\ \hline \end{array}$$

28.
$$\begin{array}{r} 10 \\ -\ 5 \\ \hline \end{array}$$

29.
$$\begin{array}{r} 14 \\ -\ 5 \\ \hline \end{array}$$

30.
$$\begin{array}{r} 13 \\ -\ 9 \\ \hline \end{array}$$

31. $15 - 9 =$ ____

32. $13 - 8 =$ ____

Circle the answer.

33. $16 - 6 = ?$
A. 7   B. 8
C. 9   D. 10

34. $15 - 8 = ?$
A. 3   B. 5
C. 7   D. 9

35. $18 - 10 = ?$
A. 6   B. 7
C. 8   D. 9

36. $8 - 0 = ?$
A. 3   B. 8
C. 5   D. 6

Part 2: Timed
Write the difference. You will have 2 minutes to complete these problems.

1. $11 - 2 =$ _____

2. $9 - 6 =$ _____

3.
$$\begin{array}{r} 5 \\ -\ 3 \\ \hline \end{array}$$

4.
$$\begin{array}{r} 8 \\ -\ 5 \\ \hline \end{array}$$

5.
$$\begin{array}{r} 13 \\ -\ 4 \\ \hline \end{array}$$

6.
$$\begin{array}{r} 14 \\ -\ 6 \\ \hline \end{array}$$

7.
$$\begin{array}{r} 12 \\ -\ 10 \\ \hline \end{array}$$

8.
$$\begin{array}{r} 10 \\ -\ 8 \\ \hline \end{array}$$

9.
$$\begin{array}{r} 14 \\ -\ 6 \\ \hline \end{array}$$

10.
$$\begin{array}{r} 17 \\ -\ 7 \\ \hline \end{array}$$

11. $13 - 10 =$ _____

12. $18 - 10 =$ _____

13. $19 - 9 =$ _____

14. $16 - 8 =$ _____

15.
$$\begin{array}{r} 16 \\ -\ 10 \\ \hline \end{array}$$

16.
$$\begin{array}{r} 9 \\ -\ 0 \\ \hline \end{array}$$

17.
$$\begin{array}{r} 11 \\ -\ 7 \\ \hline \end{array}$$

18.
$$\begin{array}{r} 13 \\ -\ 5 \\ \hline \end{array}$$

19. $16 - 9 =$ _____

20. $11 - 10 =$ _____

One Less, 10 Less

One Less and 10 Less

Use the number line for Problems 1–4.

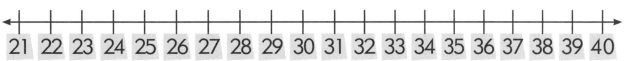

21 22 23 24 25 26 27 28 29 30 31 32 33 34 35 36 37 38 39 40

1. What number is 1 more than 27? _____

2. What number is 1 less than 27? _____

3. What number is 1 more than 30? _____

4. What number is 1 less than 30? _____

Use the number line for Problems 5 and 6.

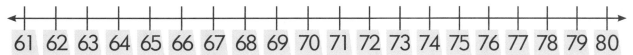

61 62 63 64 65 66 67 68 69 70 71 72 73 74 75 76 77 78 79 80

5. What number is 1 less than 74? _____

6. What number is 1 less than 79? _____

Write the number that is 1 less than the given number.

7. 83 _____   **8.** 44 _____   **9.** 16 _____

T R Y   I T

Use the Hundred Chart for Problems 10–13.

10. What number is 10 more than 18? _____

11. What number is 10 less than 18? _____

12. What number is 10 less than 41? _____

13. What number is 10 more than 39? _____

Write the number that is 10 less than the given number.

14. 59 _____   **15.** 21 _____   **16.** 94 _____

Write the answer.

17. What number is 10 less than 39? _____

18. What number is 10 less than 70? _____

19. What number is 10 more than 45? _____

20. What number is 10 more than 33? _____

Counting Back and Other Strategies

Step Back

Use the ribbon number line to find the difference.

Example: $15 - 3 = \underline{12}$

Stand on the number 15. To subtract 3, take 3 steps toward 0. Count back aloud by ones as you step toward 0. Remember to count the step (space) from 15 to 14 as "1."

You landed on 12, so the difference is 12.

---

1. $18 - 5 = \underline{}$

2. $18 - 3 = \underline{}$

3. $19 - 3 = \underline{}$

4. $17 - 6 = \underline{}$

5. $15 - 4 = \underline{}$

6. $5 - 3 = \underline{}$

7. $19 - 2 = \underline{}$

8. $10 - 5 = \underline{}$

LEARN

Use the number line to find the difference.
Draw arcs when you count back.

9. 17 − 4 = _____

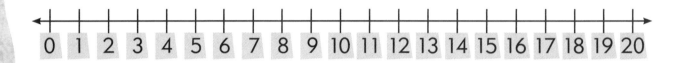

10. 20 − 3 = _____

11. 16 − 2 = _____

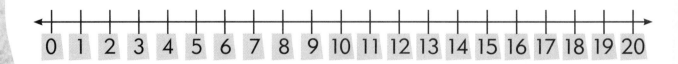

L E A R N

Counting Back and Other Strategies

Subtraction Strategies

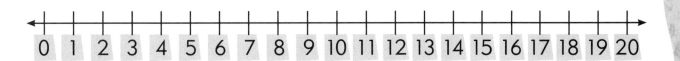

0 1 2 3 4 5 6 7 8 9 10 11 12 13 14 15 16 17 18 19 20

Write the difference. Explain the strategy that you used.

1. $12 - 4 =$ _____

2. $16 - 9 =$ _____

3. $8 - 3 =$ _____

4. $6 - 6 =$ _____

5. $19 - 5 =$ _____

6. $13 - 5 =$ _____

LEARN

```
◄─┼──┼──┼──┼──┼──┼──┼──┼──┼──┼──┼──┼──┼──┼──┼──┼──┼──┼──┼──┼──►
  0  1  2  3  4  5  6  7  8  9 10 11 12 13 14 15 16 17 18 19 20
```

7. $10 - 6 = \underline{\hspace{2cm}}$ **8.** $11 - 7 = \underline{\hspace{2cm}}$

9. $17 - 5 = \underline{\hspace{2cm}}$ **10.** $19 - 6 = \underline{\hspace{2cm}}$

11. $18 - 9 = \underline{\hspace{2cm}}$ **12.** $15 - 6 = \underline{\hspace{2cm}}$

13. $17 - 0 = \underline{\hspace{2cm}}$ **14.** $18 - 3 = \underline{\hspace{2cm}}$

15. $20 - 6 = \underline{\hspace{2cm}}$ **16.** $19 - 7 = \underline{\hspace{2cm}}$

LEARN

Counting Back and Other Strategies

Subtract

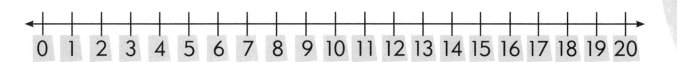

Write the difference. Explain the strategy you used.

1. 17 − 4 = _____

2. 18 − 4 = _____

3. 13 − 6 = _____

4. 12 − 8 = _____

5. 19 − 3 = _____

6. 20 − 9 = _____

7. 15 − 7 = _____

8. 6 − 6 = _____

TRY IT

**Use the number line to find the difference.
Draw arcs when you count back.**

9. $20 - 7 = $ _____

10. $16 - 7 = $ _____

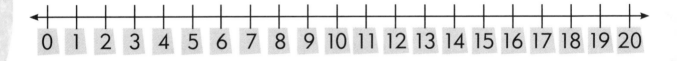

11. Charles has 15 marbles. Count back to see
how many marbles he will have if he gives away
5 of them.

_____ marbles

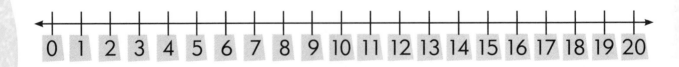

Use Strategies to Subtract

Subtraction

Write the difference. Explain the strategy you used. Use the number line if you need help.

1. $14 - 3 =$ _____

2. $18 - 5 =$ _____

3. $16 - 10 =$ _____

4. $18 - 4 =$ _____

5. $18 - 5 =$ _____

6. $19 - 6 =$ _____

7. $14 - 9 =$ _____

8. $20 - 17 =$ _____

TRY IT

Use the number line to solve.

9. What subtraction problem would you solve if you counted back 5 from 17?

_____

10. Lisa has 13 trading cards. Count back to see how many trading cards she will have if she gives away 6 trading cards.

_____

11. Start at 20 and count back 9 to find the difference.

    $20 - 9 = $ _____

Circle the answer.

12. Which problem would you solve if you counted back 10 from 19?

    A. $10 - 19 = ?$ B. $19 - 10 = ?$
    C. $20 - 10 = ?$ D. $10 - 10 = ?$

13. $8 - 5 = ?$

    A. 5   B. 8
    C. 0   D. 3

Unit Review

Checkpoint Practice

Write the number that is 1 less than the given number.

1. 9 _____   **2.** 14 _____   **3.** 36 _____

4. 52 _____   **5.** 49 _____   **6.** 90 _____

Write the number that is 10 less than the given number.

7. 13 _____   **8.** 40 _____   **9.** 76 _____

10. 97 _____   **11.** 38 _____   **12.** 62 _____

Use the number line to solve Problems 13 and 14.

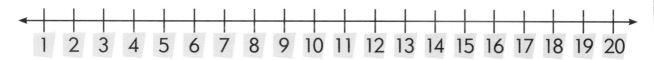

1 2 3 4 5 6 7 8 9 10 11 12 13 14 15 16 17 18 19 20

13. Count back from 14 to solve the problem.

$$14 - 8 = \underline{\quad}$$

14. Count back from 16 to solve the problem.

$$16 - 3 = \underline{\quad}$$

UNIT REVIEW

Solve.

15. Count back from 20 to solve the problem.

$20 - 10 =$ _____

16. Count back from 13 to solve the problem.

$13 - 5 =$ _____

17. What subtraction problem would you solve if you counted back 4 from 9?

_____

18. What subtraction problem would you solve if you counted back 7 from 20?

_____

Use a strategy you have learned, or math facts, to solve. Explain what you did.

19. $17 - 3 =$ _____

20. $25 - 6 =$ _____

21. $20 - 3 =$ _____

Semester Review

Checkpoint Practice

Read the problem and follow the directions.

1. Shade the numbers on the chart to show counting by 5s.

									50
51	52	53	54	55	56	57	58	59	60
61	62	63	64	65	66	67	68	69	70
71	72	73	74	75	76	77	78	79	80
81	82	83	84	85	86	87	88	89	90
91	92	93	94	95	96	97	98	99	100

2. Write the missing number. 96, 97, 98, 99, _____

3. Look at the numbers below.
Circle the symbol that belongs in the box.

83 ☐ 93

A. >   B. <   C. =

4. Write a number sentence that shows that 15 is the same as $15 + 0$.

_____

5. What number is 10 less than 56?

_____

6. Write the sum.

$$\begin{array}{r} 1 \\ 6 \\ + 8 \\ \hline \end{array}$$

7. Write the missing number.

____ $+ 5 = 8$

Circle the answer.

8. About what time does the clock show?

A. about 12:30

B. about 1:30

C. about 2:30

9. Which expression is equal to $15 - 4$?

A. $15 + 4$

B. $4 + 5$

C. $10 + 1$

10. 87 is 10 more than which number?

A. 78

B. 77

C. 97

D. 79

11. Circle the crayon that is to the right of the green crayon.

Same Number Different Ways

Numbers Different Ways

Use cubes to model each number **two** different ways.

1. 13

2. 19

Use addition or subtraction to write **two** expressions that equal the number or expression.

3. 12   _____   _____

4. $5 + 5$ _____   _____

5. $10 - 7$ _____   _____

Read the problem and follow the directions.

6. $20 - 6 = 14$. What other ways can you show 14, using only two numbers? Write **three** ways. Use subtraction for at least one of your answers.

_____   _____   _____

T R Y I T

7. Draw two other pictures that show the same number as this picture shows.

8. The picture uses addition to show 9. Draw a subtraction picture that shows 9.

Draw an addition picture and a subtraction picture to show the number.

9. 14

10. 17

TRY IT

Represent Numbers Different Ways

Show a Number Three Ways

Show the number in **three** different ways.
Make a model to show one way.
Draw a picture to show another way.
Write a subtraction expression to show the third way.
You may use addition or subtraction for your model and drawing.

1. 10 _____

2. 4 _____

3. 13 _____

LEARN

4. 6 _____

5. 3 _____

6. 14 _____

7. 5 _____

8. 12 _____

LEARN

Represent Numbers Different Ways

Show Numbers Different Ways

Read the problem and follow the directions.

1. Use cubes to make a model to show the same number as the picture shows. Then write an expression to show the same number.

 _____

2. $19 - 5$ is equal to 14.
   Write **three** other expressions that show 14.

   _____   _____   _____

3. The picture uses subtraction to show 5.
   Draw a different subtraction picture that shows 5.

TRY IT

Make a model, draw a picture, and write an expression to show the number. Only one of the three ways should use addition.

4. 16 _____

5. 19 _____

Circle the answer.

6. Which shows the same number as this picture?

A. ◻◻◻✕✕✕✕

B. ◻◻◻✕✕✕✕✕✕

C. ◻◻◻◻◻◻◻◻✕✕✕✕✕

D. ◻◻◻◻◻✕✕✕✕✕✕

7. Which expression equals 17 − 4?

A. 17 + 4

B. 4 + 7

C. 12 + 1

TRY IT

Missing Parts in Subtraction Sentences

What Number Is Missing?

Write the missing number.

1. $13 - 6 =$ _____

2. $9 -$ _____ $= 6$

3. $12 - 3 =$ _____

4. $18 - 4 =$ _____

5. $20 -$ _____ $= 14$

6. $17 -$ _____ $= 13$

7. $6 -$ _____ $= 2$

8. $14 - 5 =$ _____

9. $16 -$ _____ $= 9$

10. $14 -$ _____ $= 11$

11. $11 -$ _____ $= 5$

12. $12 -$ _____ $= 7$

T R Y   I T

Circle the missing number.

13. $8 - 2 = ?$

    A. 10   B. 2

    C. 6   D. 14

14. $7 - ? = 1$

    A. 8   B. 6

    C. 7   D. 13

15. $9 - 4 = ?$

    A. 13   B. 14

    C. 4   D. 5

16. $5 - ? = 1$

    A. 4   B. 9

    C. 6   D. 5

17. $9 - 3 = ?$

    A. 9   B. 3

    C. 6   D. 12

18. $19 - ? = 10$

    A. 1   B. 9

    C. 10   D. 10

Write the missing number.

19. $9 - 2 = \boxed{}$ **20.** $6 - \boxed{} = 3$ **21.** $4 - \boxed{} = 0$

TRY IT

Subtract with Missing Numbers

Missing Numbers

Write the missing number.

1. $14 - 8 =$ _____

2. $12 - 4 =$ _____

3. $17 - 5 =$ _____

4. $6 -$ _____ $= 3$

5. $10 = 15 -$ _____

6. $20 -$ _____ $= 17$

7. $5 -$ _____ $= 3$

8. $5 = 13 -$ _____

9. $12 -$ _____ $= 7$

10. $18 - 10 =$ _____

11. $9 -$ _____ $= 2$

12. $3 = 7 -$ _____

TRY IT

Circle the missing number.

13. $? = 9 - 3$

    A. 12   B. 2

    C. 6   D. 10

14. $3 - ? = 0$

    A. 2   B. 1

    C. 0   D. 3

15. $10 - 4 = ?$

    A. 3   B. 4

    C. 5   D. 6

16. $7 = 10 - ?$

    A. 2   B. 3

    C. 4   D. 5

17. $8 - ? = 1$

    A. 9   B. 8

    C. 7   D. 6

18. $9 - 5 = ?$

    A. 3   B. 4

    C. 5   D. 6

19. $6 - ? = 4$

    A. 4   B. 3

    C. 2   D. 1

20. $8 - 2 = ?$

    A. 2   B. 4

    C. 6   D. 10

TRY IT

Unit Review

Checkpoint Practice

Use cubes to model the number **two** different ways.

1. 12

2. 5

3. 17

Draw **two** different sketches that equal the picture or number. Use subtraction for at least one sketch.

4.

5. 12

Write **two** expressions that equal the model, picture, or expression. Use subtraction for at least one expression.

6. _____ _____

7. _____ _____

8. $4 + 10$

_____ _____

Show a model for the number. Then draw a picture and write an expression.

9. 9

_____

10. 20

_____

Write the missing number.

11. $12 -$ _____ $= 5$

12. $7 - 4 =$ _____

13. $9 = 10 -$ _____

14. $15 - 6 =$ _____

15. $20 - 7 =$ _____

16. $3 = 9 -$ _____

17. $14 -$ _____ $= 7$

18. $12 = 16 -$ _____

Circle the answer.

19. Which shows the same number as the picture?

A.

B.

C.

D.

20. Which other picture also shows 13?

A. ● ● ● ● ● ● + ● ● ● ● ● ●

B. ● ● ● ● + ● ● ● + ● ● ● ● ● ●

C. ● + ● ● ●

D. ● ● ● ● ● + ● ● ● ● ● + ● ●

21. Which expression is equal to $15 - 4$?

    A. $15 + 4$ B. $4 + 5$ C. $10 + 1$

Read the problem and follow the directions.

22. $9 - 4 = 5$. Using different numbers, show another way to write 5.

                 _____

Write or circle the missing number.

23. $9 = 11 - $ _____

24. $8 - 2 = ?$

    A. 8   B. 6   C. 2

Coins

Practice Coins

Circle the name of each coin.

1.

   A. penny   B. nickel

   C. dime   D. quarter

2.

   A. penny   B. nickel

   C. dime   D. quarter

3.

   A. penny   B. nickel

   C. dime   D. quarter

4.

   A. penny   B. nickel

   C. dime   D. quarter

Circle the coin with the given value.

5. 10 cents

   A.   B.

   C.   D.

6. 25 cents

   A.   B.

   C.   D.

TRY IT

Choose the value of the coin.

7.

    A. 1 cent

    B. 5 cents

    C. 10 cents

    D. 25 cents

8.

    A. 1 cent

    B. 5 cents

    C. 10 cents

    D. 25 cents

Circle the coin that there is most of.

9.

    A. penny   B. dime

    C. nickel   D. quarter

10.

    A. penny   B. dime

    C. nickel   D. quarter

Write how many of the given coin is shown.

11. penny

_____

12. dime

_____

TRY IT

Identify Coins

Coins and Values

Circle the name of the coin.

1.

   A. penny   B. nickel

   C. dime   D. quarter

2.

   A. penny   B. nickel

   C. dime   D. quarter

Circle the coin with the given value.

3. 25 cents

A.   B.

C.   D.

4. 5 cents

A.   B.

C.   D.

Write how many of the given coin is shown.

5. penny

_____

6. nickel

_____

TRY IT

Read the problem and follow the directions.

7. Circle the nickel.

A.   B.

C.   D.

8. Circle the quarter.

A.   B.

C.   D.

---

9. Underline all the dimes.

---

10. Circle the value of this coin.

A. 1 cent

B. 5 cents

C. 10 cents

D. 25 cents

11. Circle the value of this coin.

A. 1 cent

B. 5 cents

C. 10 cents

D. 25 cents

---

12. Carla has a coin worth 25 cents. Which coin does she have? Circle it.

A.    B.   C.   D.

   quarter   penny   dime   nickel

TRY IT

Equal Money Amounts

Same Value Coin Groups

Count by 10s, 5s, or ones to find the value of the group of coins. Write the value on the line.

1.    _____ cents

2.    _____ cents

3.    _____ cents

Circle the group of coins with the same value as the first coin shown.

4.   A.    B.

5.   A.    B.

6.   A.    B.

TRY IT

Circle the answer.

7. Sam has the money shown. Which answer choice shows the same amount of money?

A.

B.

C.

D.

8. Austin has this coin in his pocket. Which answer choice shows the same amount of money?

A.

B.

C.

D.

Use your coins for Problems 9 and 10.

9. Write the value of this coin. Then use different coins to show the same amount.

_____ cents

10. Show two ways to make 25 cents.

Measure and Compare Length

Measurement Practice

Circle the longer object. Underline the shorter object.

1.

2.

Write the length of the fork in paper clips.

3.

about _____ paper clips

Measure each object with paper clips. Write the length in paper clips.

4. craft stick

   about _____ paper clips

5. crayon

   about _____ paper clips

6. About how much longer is the craft stick than the crayon?

   about _____ paper clips

7. About how much shorter is the crayon than the craft stick?

   about _____ paper clips

T R Y   I T

Circle the answer.

8. Which object is longer?

A.

B.

9. How many squares wide is the book?

A. 5   B. 6   C. 4   D. 7

10. How many paper clips longer is the feather than the caterpillar?

A. 2   B. 3   C. 4   D. 9

TRY IT

Weight

Which Is Heavier?

Circle the answer.

1. Which object is lighter?

A.    B. (cube) = (7 cubes)

2. Which object is heavier?

A. (mug) = (15 teddy bears)   B. (marble) = (12 teddy bears)

3. Which object is heavier?

A. (spoon) = (6 paper clips)   B. (doll) = (9 paper clips)

4. Which object is lighter?

A. (tennis ball) = (8 squares)   B. (baseball) = (9 squares)

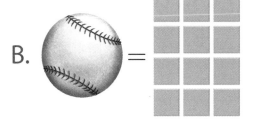

TRY IT

Use the balance to compare the weights of the two objects. For the orange, you may use a fruit of similar weight. Circle the answer.

5. Which is heavier?

    A. circle block

    B. pencil

6. Which is lighter?

    A. orange

    B. crayon

Hold one object in each hand to compare their weights. Circle the answer.

7. Which object is lighter?

    A. paper clip

    B. spoon

8. Which object is heavier?

    A. circle block

    B. shoe

TRY IT

Capacity and Volume

Holds More, Holds Less

Circle the container that holds more. Underline the one that holds less.

1.

 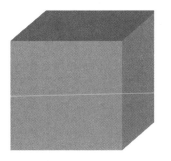

2.

3.

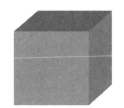

TRY IT

4.

5.

6.

TRY IT

Unit Review

Checkpoint Practice

Read the problem and follow the directions.

1. Measure the straw with paper clips.
    Write the length.

    about _____ paper clips

2. Weigh the eraser with a balance and circle
    blocks. Write the weight.

    about _____ circles

3. Circle the container that holds more.
    Underline the one that holds less.

4. Write the value of the coin.

    _____ cent

Circle the answer.

5. What is the name of the coin?

    A. penny   B. nickel

    C. dime   D. quarter

UNIT REVIEW

6. What is the value of the coin?

A. 1 cent

B. 5 cents

C. 10 cents

D. 25 cents

7. Look at the coins.

Whose coins add up to the same amount as 5 nickels?

A. Lana

B. Barry

C. Pedro

D. Flora

8. Which object is shorter?

A.

B.

---

9. How many squares wide is the paper?

A. 6   B. 7

C. 8   D. 9

---

10. How many paper clips longer is the snake than the caterpillar?

A. 3   B. 4   C. 7   D. 11

---

11. Which of these glasses would hold more water?

A.   B.

12. Some students used a balance and some snap cubes to weigh a pencil and a toy car. Which object weighs more?

A. pencil

B. toy car

13. Sam has the money shown.

Which answer choice shows the same amount of money?

A.

B.

C.

D.

Tens, Ones, and Estimation

Group and Count Tens and Ones

Circle groups of 10 objects. Tell how many tens and ones there are. Then count by 10s and 1s to find the total number of objects. Write the number on the line.

1.

_____ stars

2.

_____ diamonds

3.

_____ suns

LEARN

4.

_____ hearts

5.

_____ circles

===

Read the problem and follow the directions.

6. Draw as many triangles as you can in 30 seconds. Try not to count as you draw the triangles. Then circle groups of 10 triangles. Tell how many tens and ones. Then count by 10s and 1s to find the number of triangles. Write the number on the line.

_____triangles

Tens, Ones, and Estimation

Count the Objects

Make as many trains of 10 cubes as you can. Count the tens and ones. Then count by 10s and 1s to find the total number of cubes. Write the answers.

1. _____ tens   _____ ones   _____ cubes

Circle groups of 10 objects. Tell how many tens and ones there are. Then count by 10s and 1s to find the total number of objects. Write the number on the line.

2.

_____ flowers

Circle the answer.

3. Count the hearts. How many tens and ones?

A. 3 tens 5 ones   B. 3 tens 3 ones

C. 5 tens 3 ones   D. 5 tens 5 ones

TRY IT

Tell about how many objects. Write the answer.

4.

about _____ hearts

5.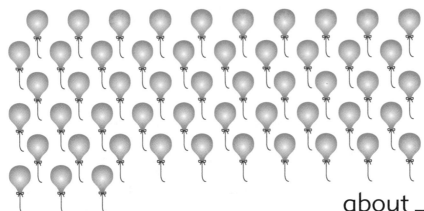

about _____ balloons

Tell about how many objects. Circle the answer.

6.

A. about 20 paper clips   B. about 30 paper clips

C. about 40 paper clips   D. about 50 paper clips

7. ✳ ✳ ✳ ✳ ✳ ✳ ✳ ✳ ✳ ✳
✳ ✳ ✳ ✳ ✳ ✳ ✳ ✳ ✳
✳

A. about 10 suns   B. about 20 suns

C. about 30 suns   D. about 40 suns

T R Y   I T

Place Value

Write Numbers as Tens and Ones

Look at the base-10 blocks. Count the tens rods.
Count the ones cubes. Write the number of tens
and ones. Say the number shown by the blocks.
Then write the number.

1.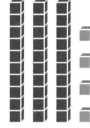

_____ tens _____ ones = _____

2.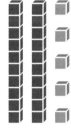

_____ tens _____ ones = _____

3.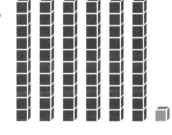

_____ tens _____ ones = _____

4.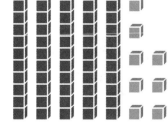

_____ tens _____ ones = _____

L E A R N

Complete the table.
Example

Base-10 Blocks	Tens	Ones	Number
	5 tens	2 ones	52
	8 tens	7 ones	87

	Base-10 Blocks	Tens	Ones	Number
5.		9 tens	0 ones	_____
6.		_____ tens	_____ ones	_____
7.		_____ tens	_____ ones	_____

Place Value

Numbers with Tens and Ones

Write the number of tens and ones. Say the number shown by the blocks. Then write the number.

1. 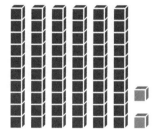 _____ tens _____ ones = _____

2. 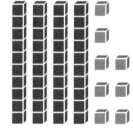 _____ tens _____ ones = _____

3. 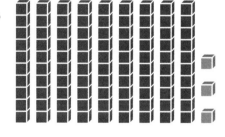 _____ tens _____ ones = _____

4. 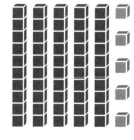 _____ tens _____ ones = _____

T R Y   I T

Circle the number that the model shows.

5.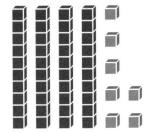

A. 44   B. 47

C. 74   D. 77

6.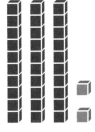

A. 5   B. 32

C. 23   D. 52

7.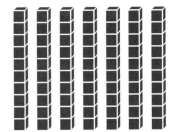

A. 7   B. 17

C. 70   D. 80

Represent Numbers

Draw Tens and Ones

Draw a model of the number using groups of tens and ones.

1. 23

2. 33

3. 19

TRY IT

4. 47

5. 56

6. 38

Place Value for Numbers

What's the Number?

Write the number of tens rods and the number of ones cubes. Then write the number that these blocks show together.

1.

_____ _____ = _____

2.

_____ _____ = _____

3.

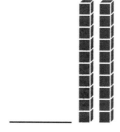

_____ _____ = _____

4.

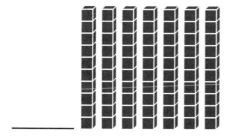

_____ _____ = _____

TRY IT

Write how many tens and how many ones are in the numbers.

5. 65 _____ tens _____ ones

6. 58 _____ tens _____ ones

7. 84 _____ tens _____ ones

8. 77 _____ tens _____ ones

Use base-10 blocks to model the number.

9. 88

10. 92

11. 48

12. 59

13. 18

14. 61

TRY IT

Model Numbers Different Ways

Model 2-Digit Numbers

Use base-10 blocks to make the model.
Then answer the problem.

1. Show 28 ones. What is
another way to show 28?   _____ tens   _____ ones

2. Show 4 tens 1 one. What is
another way to show 41?   _____ tens   _____ ones

Use base-10 blocks to model the number three
different ways. Write the number of tens and
ones in each model.

3. 67   _____ tens   _____ ones

_____ tens   _____ ones   _____ tens   _____ ones

4. 30
                                                    _____ tens   _____ ones

_____ tens   _____ ones   _____ tens   _____ ones

5. 79
                                                    _____ tens   _____ ones

_____ tens   _____ ones   _____ tens   _____ ones

TRY IT

Circle the model that shows the same number as the given model.

6.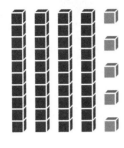

A.

B.

C.

D.

7.

A.

B.

C.

D.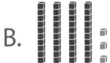

8.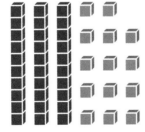

A.

B.

C.

D. (model)

Use Objects to Add

Addition with Objects

Build each number with base-10 blocks on a place-value mat. Then add and write the sum.

Example

$24 + 51 = \underline{75}$

Hundreds	Tens	Ones

1. $30 + 49 = \underline{\hspace{2em}}$

2. $67 + 21 = \underline{\hspace{2em}}$

3. $13 + 41 = \underline{\hspace{2em}}$

TRY IT

4. $32 + 64 = $ _____

5. $75 + 12 = $ _____

6. $41 + 11 = $ _____

7. $32 + 12 = $ _____

8. $40 + 23 = $ _____

Hundreds	Tens	Ones

TRY IT

Use Sketches to Add

Sketch to Add

Sketch squares to show each addend.
Circle groups of 10.
Then count by 10s and 1s to add. Write the sum.

1. $23 + 16 =$ _____

2. $14 + 32 =$ _____

Sketch base-10 blocks to show each addend.
Then count by 10s and 1s to add.
Write the sum.

3. $46 + 53 =$ _____

4. $32 + 57 =$ _____

5. $63 + 11 =$ _____

TRY IT

Make a sketch to solve the problem. Write the sum.

6. $13 + 14 = $ _____

7. $18 + 51 = $ _____

8. $26 + 62 = $ _____

Addition with Sums Through 100

Sums Through 100

Add. You may use base-10 blocks to help you.

1.   44
      $+\ 9$

2.   59
      $+\ 5$

3.   81
      $+\ 9$

4. $28 + 9 =$ _____

5. _____ $= 53 + 6$

6. $93 + 7 =$ _____

TRY IT

7.
$$\begin{array}{r} 16 \\ +\ 5 \\ \hline \end{array}$$

8.
$$\begin{array}{r} 28 \\ +\ 7 \\ \hline \end{array}$$

Circle the answer. You may use base-10 blocks to help you.

9.
$$\begin{array}{r} 79 \\ +\ 3 \\ \hline \end{array}$$

A. 82   B. 76

C. 78   D. 80

10.
$$\begin{array}{r} 88 \\ +\ 4 \\ \hline \end{array}$$

A. 44   B. 84

C. 29   D. 92

TRY IT

Different Ways to Add

Add Different Ways

Explain how the student found the sum.

1. This is how Jenna added 49 + 4:

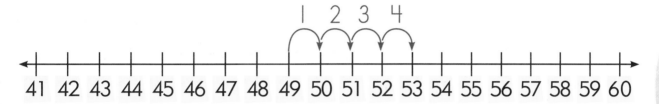

2. This is how Mark added 34 + 9:

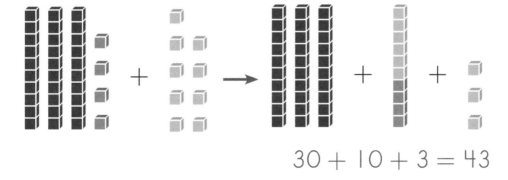

$$30 + 10 + 3 = 43$$

TRY IT

3. This is how Anna added $57 + 3$:

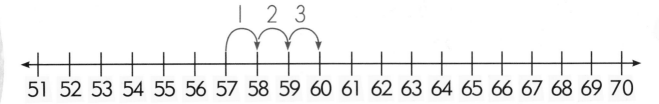

Add. You may use a number line, base-10 blocks, or ten-frames. Explain how you found the sum.

4. $36 + 9 = $ _____

5. $58 + 5 = $ _____

6. $84 + 7 = $ _____

7. $78 + 4 = $ _____

8. $47 + 6 = $ _____

9. $72 + 8 = $ _____

TRY IT

Use Objects to Subtract

Subtract with Objects

Use circles and cups to show the problem. Then write the difference.

1. 35 – 23 = _____

2. 42 – 12 = _____

3. 57 – 32 = _____

TRY IT

Use base-10 blocks and a place-value mat to show the problem. Then write the difference.

4. $97 - 53 = \underline{\hspace{2em}}$

5. $79 - 63 = \underline{\hspace{2em}}$

6. $84 - 33 = \underline{\hspace{2em}}$

7. $37 - 22 = \underline{\hspace{2em}}$

8. $27 - 12 = \underline{\hspace{2em}}$

9. $53 - 12 = \underline{\hspace{2em}}$

10. $78 - 24 = \underline{\hspace{2em}}$

11. $86 - 33 = \underline{\hspace{2em}}$

Hundreds	Tens	Ones

TRY IT

Use Sketches to Subtract

Sketch to Subtract

Sketch base-10 blocks to show the subtraction problem. Cross out tens rods and ones cubes to subtract. Write the difference.

1. $95 - 41 =$ _____

2. $73 - 53 =$ _____

TRY IT

Circle the answer.

3. Which picture shows 39 – 6?

A.

B.

C.

4. Which picture shows 27 – 5?

A.

B.

C.

TRY IT

Subtraction with Regrouping

Find the Difference

Find the difference. Use base-10 blocks and a place-value mat to model the problem. Regroup when necessary.

1. $\begin{array}{r} 26 \\ -\ 7 \\ \hline \end{array}$

2. $\begin{array}{r} 31 \\ -\ 9 \\ \hline \end{array}$

3. $\begin{array}{r} 18 \\ -\ 4 \\ \hline \end{array}$

4. $\begin{array}{r} 23 \\ -\ 6 \\ \hline \end{array}$

5. $\begin{array}{r} 34 \\ -\ 6 \\ \hline \end{array}$

6. $\begin{array}{r} 32 \\ -\ 8 \\ \hline \end{array}$

7. $28 - 9 =$ _____

8. _____ $= 33 - 7$

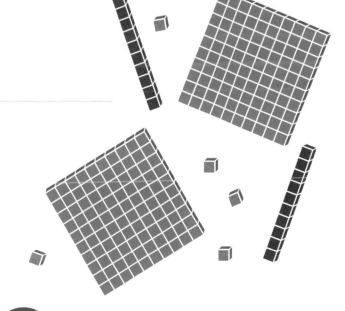

TRY IT

9.   21
    − 4

10.   29
    − 5

11.   33
    − 4

12.   40
    − 3

13.   22
    − 9

14.   25
    − 3

15.   28
    − 9

16.   15
    − 9

17.   21
    − 2

18.   25
    − 9

19. _____ $= 39 - 6$

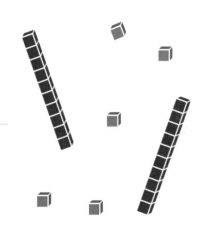

20. $26 - 8 =$ _____

More Subtraction with Regrouping

Practice Subtraction with Regrouping

Subtract. You may use base-10 blocks and a place-value mat to help you.

1.
$$\begin{array}{r} 54 \\ -\ \ 8 \\ \hline \end{array}$$

2.
$$\begin{array}{r} 81 \\ -\ \ 3 \\ \hline \end{array}$$

3.
$$\begin{array}{r} 47 \\ -\ \ 6 \\ \hline \end{array}$$

4.
$$\begin{array}{r} 75 \\ -\ \ 7 \\ \hline \end{array}$$

5.
$$\begin{array}{r} 94 \\ -\ \ 6 \\ \hline \end{array}$$

6.
$$\begin{array}{r} 67 \\ -\ \ 9 \\ \hline \end{array}$$

7.
$$\begin{array}{r} 58 \\ -\ \ 7 \\ \hline \end{array}$$

8.
$$\begin{array}{r} 82 \\ -\ \ 9 \\ \hline \end{array}$$

9.
$$\begin{array}{r} 72 \\ -\ \ 4 \\ \hline \end{array}$$

10.
$$\begin{array}{r} 60 \\ -\ \ 3 \\ \hline \end{array}$$

11.
$$\begin{array}{r} 93 \\ -\ \ 5 \\ \hline \end{array}$$

12.
$$\begin{array}{r} 44 \\ -\ \ 8 \\ \hline \end{array}$$

TRY IT

13. $66 - 4 =$ _____

14. _____ $= 83 - 7$

15. _____ $= 92 - 3$

16. $56 - 9 =$ _____

17. $71 - 9 =$ _____

18. _____ $= 81 - 2$

Circle the answer. You may use base-10 blocks and a place-value mat to help you.

19.
$$\begin{array}{r} 82 \\ -\ 4 \\ \hline \end{array}$$

A. 78

B. 86

C. 84

D. 92

20.
$$\begin{array}{r} 92 \\ -\ 8 \\ \hline \end{array}$$

A. 100

B. 96

C. 48

D. 84

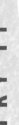

TRY IT

Different Ways to Subtract

Subtract Different Ways

Explain how the student found the difference.

1. This is how Bobby subtracted 66 − 8:

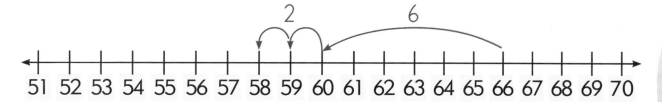

2. This is how Gina subtracted 54 − 7:

   $(40 + 14) - 7$

   $40 + (14 - 7)$

   $40 + 7 = 47$

   $54 - 7 = 47$

3. Lauren subtracted 94 − 5 using a number line. Explain how she could have used the number line to find the answer.

TRY IT

Subtract. You may use a number line.
Explain how you found the difference.

4. 56 – 9 = ____

5. 23 – 5 = ____

6. 91 – 4 = ____

7. 33 – 7 = ____

Circle the answer.

8. This is how Vani subtracted 71 – 7:

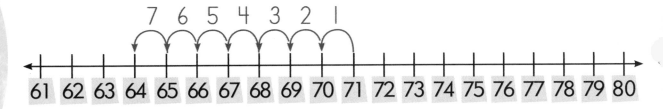

Which strategy did Vani use? Circle the answer.

A. She counted back from the greater number.

B. She broke apart the greater number into numbers that were easier to work with.

C. She first subtracted the tens and then the ones.

TRY IT

Add and Subtract

Use Strategies

Circle the way you would solve the problem.
Tell why.

1. $23 + 5$

Strategy 1:
Count on from the greater number.

Start at 23. Count on 5.
24, 25, 26, 27, 28

So $23 + 5 = 28$.

Strategy 2:
Count on from the lesser number.

Start at 5. Count on 23.
6, 7, 8, 9, 10, 11, 12, 13, 14, 15, 16, 17, 18, 19,
20, 21, 22, 23, 24, 25, 26, 27, 28

So $23 + 5 = 28$.

Solve. You may use any strategy you like.
Then explain why you chose your strategy.

2. $52 - 7 =$ _____

3. $5 + 67 =$ _____

TRY IT

Circle the way you would solve the problem. Tell why.

4. 94 − 6

Strategy 1:
Think of easier numbers.

Subtract 94 − 4 to get 90. Since 6 is equal to 4 + 2, you can subtract 2 from 90 to get 88.

So 94 − 6 = 88.

Strategy 2:
Take 9 tens rods and 4 ones cubes.
Regroup 1 tens rod as 10 ones cubes.
Take away 6 ones cubes from 14 ones cubes.

You now have 8 tens rods and 8 ones cubes.

So 94 − 6 = 88.

Say the answer.

5. Hannah subtracted 12 − 2 using a number line. Explain how she could have used the number line to find the answer.

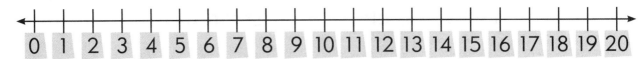

Circle the answer.

6. This is how Pete solved 88 − 4:

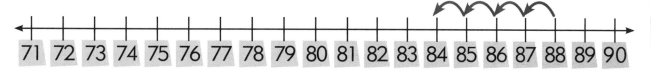

Which strategy did Pete use?

A. He counted back from the greater number.

B. He broke apart the greater number into numbers that were easier to work with.

C. He first subtracted the tens and then the ones.

7. This is how Ana solved 39 + 7:

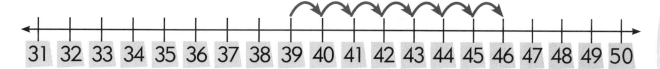

Which strategy did Ana use?

A. She first added the ones, then added the tens, and then added both numbers together.

B. She took enough from the lesser number to increase the greater number to the next ten, and then added the remaining ones.

C. She counted on from the greater number.

TRY IT

8. This is how Tanya solved $53 - 7$:

Step 1: $(40 + 13) - 7$

Step 2: $40 + (13 - 7)$

Step 3: $40 + 6 = 46$

Which strategy did Tanya use?

A. She counted back from the greater number.

B. She broke apart the greater number into numbers that were easier to work with.

C. She first subtracted the tens and then the ones.

Say the answer.

9. This is how Callie solved $58 - 9$:

Step 1: $(40 + 18) - 9$

Step 2: $40 + (18 - 9)$

Step 3: $40 + 9 = 49$

Explain how she solved the problem.

TRY IT

Unit Review

Checkpoint Practice

Read the problem and follow the directions.

1. Grace subtracted 28 − 7 using a number line. Explain how she could have used the number line to find the answer.

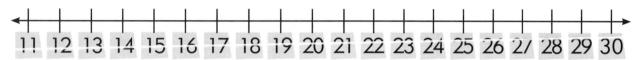

_____

2. Write the number of tens and ones.

_____ tens   _____ ones

3. Use base-10 blocks to model the number three different ways. Write the number of tens and ones in each model.

53

_____ tens   _____ ones

_____ tens   _____ ones

_____ tens   _____ ones

UNIT REVIEW

Add or subtract. You may use base-10 blocks, sketches, or another strategy.

4.
$$\begin{array}{r} 28 \\ +9 \\ \hline \end{array}$$

5.
$$\begin{array}{r} 52 \\ -9 \\ \hline \end{array}$$

6. _____ $= 59 + 6$

7. $95 - 6 =$ _____

Make a sketch to solve the problem.

8. $28 - 17 =$ _____

Circle the answer.

9. About how many stars are shown?

  A. about 10

  B. about 20

  C. about 30

  D. about 40

10. Sally counted the apples and grouped them as tens and ones.

How many tens and ones does she have?

  A. 1 ten and 2 ones

  B. 2 tens and 1 one

  C. 3 ones

  D. 3 tens

11. About how many triangles are shown?

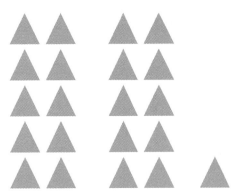

    A. about 10

    B. about 20

    C. about 30

    D. about 40

12. If I have 4 tens and 5 ones, what number do I have?

    A. 9

    B. 45

    C. 54

    D. 90

13.
$$57$$
$$+\ \ 5$$

    A. 52

    B. 62

    C. 63

    D. 72

14. $63 - 7 = $ _____

    A. 54

    B. 56

    C. 64

    D. 66

Add and Subtract with Base-10 Models

Base-10 Blocks and Sketches

Use base-10 blocks to solve the problem.

1. $33 + 29 =$ _____

Draw a sketch to solve the problem.

2. $49 + 2 =$ _____

Use base-10 blocks to solve the problem.

3. $33 + 9 =$ _____

4. $46 + 42 =$ _____

TRY IT

Draw a sketch to solve the problem.

5. $13 + 15 =$ _____

Use base-10 blocks to solve the problem.

6. $33 + 33 =$ _____

Draw a sketch to solve the problem.

7. $31 - 9 =$ _____

Use base-10 blocks to solve the problem.

8. $87 - 43 =$ _____

Draw a sketch of base-10 blocks and use it to solve the problem.

9. $98 - 53 =$ _____

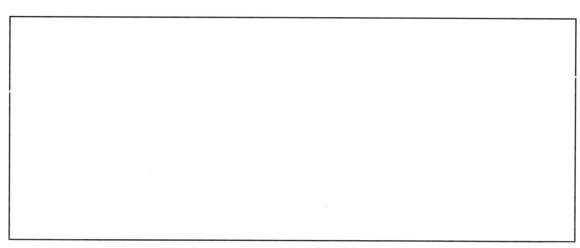

Use base-10 blocks to solve the problem.

10. $61 - 29 =$ _____

Draw a sketch of base-10 blocks to solve the problem.

11. $36 - 21 =$ _____

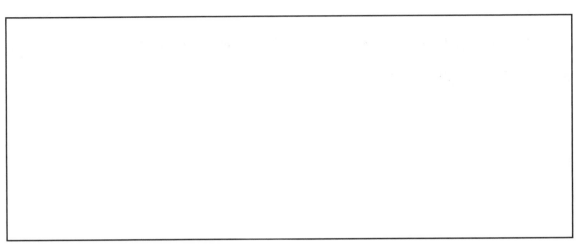

Draw a sketch to solve the problem.

12. $46 - 22 =$ _____

Solve Compare and Change Problems

Solving with Sketches and Models

Draw a sketch to help solve the problem.

1. 45 − 43 = _____

2. 85 − 43 = _____

3. _____ = 96 − 65

T R Y   I T

4. $83 - 21 = $ _____

5. _____ $= 65 - 20$

Use base-10 blocks to help solve the problem.

6. $27 - 9 = $ _____

7. _____ $= 45 + 21$

8. $79 - 35 = $ _____

TRY IT

Part-Part-Total Problems

More Uses of Part-Part-Total

Use the Part-Part-Total Sheet and circle blocks to solve Problems 1 and 2. Then complete the number sentence and write the missing part.

1. There are 16 coins in a jar.
   9 of the coins are nickels. The rest are pennies.

   How many pennies are in the jar?

   $9 +$ _____ $= 16$ _____ pennies

2. Olivia has 24 beads. 17 of the beads are in a bag.
   The rest of the beads are on the table.

   How many beads are on the table?

   $17 +$ _____ $= 24$ _____ beads

Use the Part-Part-Total Sheet and base-10 blocks to solve Problems 3 and 4. Then complete the number sentence and write the missing part.

3. There are 28 stickers.
   15 of the stickers are squares.
   The rest of the stickers are triangles.

   How many stickers are triangles?

   $15 +$ _____ $= 28$ _____ stickers

LEARN

4. A bag has 26 marbles. 19 of them are striped.
The rest are not striped.

How many marbles are **not** striped?

$19 + \underline{\hspace{2cm}} = 26$ $\underline{\hspace{2cm}}$ marbles

---

Write a number sentence for the story problem.
Use a ? for the missing part. Then use the Part-
Part-Total Sheet and base-10 blocks to solve.
Write the answer.

5. A puzzle has 33 pieces.
There are 21 pieces on the table.
The rest of the pieces are in the box.

How many pieces are in the box?

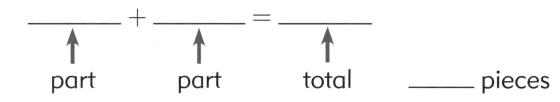

$\underline{\hspace{2cm}} + \underline{\hspace{2cm}} = \underline{\hspace{2cm}}$

part   part   total $\underline{\hspace{1.5cm}}$ pieces

6. A jar holds 66 buttons.
52 of the buttons are circles.
The rest of the buttons are other shapes.

How many buttons are other shapes?

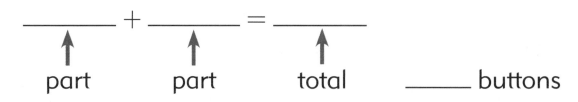

$\underline{\hspace{2cm}} + \underline{\hspace{2cm}} = \underline{\hspace{2cm}}$

part   part   total $\underline{\hspace{1.5cm}}$ buttons

LEARN

Part-Part-Total Problems

Combine Story Problems

Use base-10 blocks or a part-part-total chart to solve the problem, if needed.

1. Evan's hens laid 10 eggs.
   4 of the eggs were brown and
   the rest were white.

   How many eggs were white?   _____

2. Heidi's garden has 14 trees.
   6 of the trees have red leaves.

   How many trees do **not** have red leaves?   _____

3. Annie bought 19 notecards.
   11 of the notecards had flowers
   on them and the rest had hearts.

   How many notecards had hearts?   _____

4. Claire rode her bike for 12 miles and
   Yael rode her bike for 19 miles.

   How many miles did they ride altogether?   _____

TRY IT

5. Heidi's garden has 11 trees.
6 trees have red leaves.
The rest have green leaves.

How many trees have green leaves? _____

6. Kyle had 13 red trucks.
Vince had 19 red trucks.

How many red trucks did the boys have
altogether? _____

7. Grant planted 29 sunflower seeds and
Daphne planted 8.

How many sunflower seeds did they
plant in all? _____

8. Izzie has 32 pennies and Mellie has
6 pennies.

How many pennies do they have in all? _____

9. Sally washed 22 cars and Janie washed
27 cars.

How many cars did they wash in all? _____

TRY IT

Problems with Parts and Total

Missing Parts in Combined Stories

Circle the answer.

1. Which of the following shows two amounts being combined?

   A. Tanya scored 15 goals in the soccer game. Helen scored 20 goals. How many more goals did Helen score than Tanya?

   B. Jake made 18 cheese pizzas and 13 mushroom pizzas for his restaurant. How many pizzas did he make in all?

   C. Kate flew her kite for 20 minutes. Tom flew his kite for 27 minutes. How much longer did Tom fly his kite than Kate did?

Solve.

2. Jesse was on vacation for 21 days. He went to the beach on 13 of the days.

   How many days did Jesse **not** go to the beach? _____

3. Becky picked 14 peaches. Three of them were not ripe. The rest were ripe.

   How many of the peaches were ripe? _____

TRY IT

4. Hal baked 15 apples.
He added sugar to 3 of them and cinnamon to the rest.

How many apples had cinnamon? _____

5. Tessie read 15 books.
Two of the books were mystery books and the rest were comedies.

How many books were comedies? _____

6. Nina baked 44 lemon bars for the bake sale.
She put 23 of them in a box.

How many lemon bars were **not** in a box? _____

7. Judy baked 24 cupcakes.
Five of the cupcakes were chocolate and the rest were vanilla.

How many cupcakes were vanilla? _____

8. Toby has 34 trains.
Ten of them are black and the rest are red.

How many trains are red? _____

Change Problems

Solve with Start-Change-Result

Use the Start-Change-Result Chart to solve.

1. Patrick had 53 stamps.
   Susan gave him 21 more stamps.

   How many stamps does Patrick
   have now?   _____

2. Patrick had 53 stamps.
   He gave Susan 21 of his stamps.

   How many stamps does Patrick
   have now?   _____

3. Patrick had 53 stamps.
   Susan gave him some more stamps.
   Patrick now has 67 stamps.

   How many stamps did Susan give
   Patrick?   _____

4. Patrick had 53 stamps.
   He gave some stamps to Susan.
   Patrick now has 31 stamps.

   How many stamps did Patrick give
   to Susan?   _____

T R Y   I T

5. Franca had 62 books.
His friends gave him more books for his birthday.
He now has 73 books.

How many books did Franca get for his birthday?   _____

6. Sherri had 36 ribbons.
She bought 9 more.

How many ribbons does Sherri have now?   _____

7. Blake had 87 nails.
He used 25 of them.

How many nails does Blake have left?   _____

8. The pancake house made 65 pancakes.
The children ate some of these pancakes.
There were 13 pancakes left.

How many pancakes did the children eat?   _____

Missing Numbers in Story Problems

What's Missing: Start, Change, Result

Fill in the start-change-result chart. Use a ? for the missing number. Then solve the problem.

1. Aaron had a stack of napkins. He took 5 napkins to set the table. Now there are 7 napkins in the stack.

   How many napkins did he have
   in the stack in the beginning?   _____ napkins

Start	+ or −	Change	=	Result

2. Brandon baked 36 muffins. His family ate 9 muffins.

   How many muffins are left?   _____ muffins

Result	=	Start	+ or −	Change

3. Julia had 18 markers. She bought 5 more markers.

   How many markers does Julia
   have now?   _____ markers

Start	+ or −	Change	=	Result

L E A R N

4. Haley has 11 grapes. Her dad gives her some more. Now Haley had has 26 grapes.

How many more grapes did her dad give her? _____ grapes

Start	+ or −	Change	=	Result

5. Rosa had some strawberries. She had to throw away 10 that got too soft. She has 32 strawberries left.

How many strawberries did Rosa have at the start? _____ strawberries

Start	+ or −	Change	=	Result

6. Ron counted 37 people at baseball practice. Then some of them left to go home. Now there are 22 people at the practice.

How many people left to go home? _____ people

Result	=	Start	+ or −	Change

Missing Numbers in Story Problems

Start, Change, and Result

Solve. Use your Start-Change-Result Chart, if needed.

1. Petra and her friends had 47 grapes.
   They ate 32 of the grapes.

   How many grapes do Petra and
   her friends have left?   _____ grapes

2. Cliff's uncle gave him 43 stamps.
   Cliff now has 65 stamps.

   How many stamps did Cliff
   have before his uncle gave
   him some stamps?   _____ stamps

3. The library had 97 storybooks last week.
   Children borrowed some of them.
   The library now has 85 storybooks.

   How many storybooks did
   the children borrow?   _____ storybooks

TRY IT

4. Kamilah had 68 coins in his collection.
He was given 21 more coins.

How many coins does
Kamilah have now? _____ coins

5. Monica had 25 markers.
She found some more.
Now she has 34 markers.

How many markers did
Monica find? _____ markers

6. After lunch, there were 13 carrot sticks
left on the plate.
The family had eaten 36 carrot sticks
for lunch.

How many carrot sticks were
on the plate before lunch? _____ carrot sticks

Comparison Story Problems

Compare Story Problems

Solve.

1. Mark has gone bowling 57 times.
   Pamela has gone bowling 34 times.

   How many more times has Mark
   gone bowling than Pamela?   _____ more

2. Jennifer has 43 comic books.
   Anne has 55 comic books.

   How many fewer comic books
   does Jennifer have than Anne?   _____ fewer

3. Julian has visited the zoo 28 times.
   Artie has visited the zoo 22 times.

   How many fewer times has Artie
   visited the zoo than Julian?   _____ fewer

4. Archie has flown on a plane 13 times.
   Elaine has flown on a plane 25 times.

   How many more times has Elaine
   flown on a plane than Archie?   _____ more

TRY IT

5. Antoine has 46 books.
Karl has 25 books.

How many more books does
Antoine have than Karl?   _____ more

6. The flower shop has 23 tulips
and 59 daffodils.

How many fewer tulips does it
have than daffodils?   _____ fewer

7. Diane has 89 crayons.
Sarah has 36 crayons.

How many fewer crayons
does Sarah have than Diane?   _____ fewer

8. Theresa painted 15 pictures.
Carol painted 67 pictures.

How many more pictures did Carol
paint than Theresa?   _____ more

TRY IT

Story Problems That Compare

Let's Compare

Solve by adding or subtracting. You may use base-10 blocks to help you.

1. Jacquie has 47 books.
   Shirley has 98 books.

   How many more books does
   Shirley have than Jacquie?   _____ books

2. Jamil has 21 trading cards.
   Frank has 36 more cards than Jamil.

   How many cards does Frank have?   _____ cards

3. Rob's team scored 45 points in
   the basketball game.
   Sam's team scored 34 points.

   How many fewer points did
   Sam's team score than Rob's
   team?   _____ points

TRY IT

4. Joan has 82 stickers.
Megan has 6 fewer stickers than Joan.

How many stickers does
Megan have?   _____ stickers

5. Margo has 23 finger puppets.
Rhea has 9 more finger puppets than
Margo.

How many finger puppets
does Rhea have?   _____ puppets

6. Geoff has 78 pennies.
Devon has 32 fewer pennies
than Geoff.

How many pennies does
Devon have?   _____ pennies

7. Ryan ran 6 laps around the
field last week.
Peter ran 24 laps around the
field last week.

How many fewer laps did
Ryan run than Peter?   _____ laps

8. The deli sold 59 turkey sandwiches.
The deli also sold 35 tuna sandwiches.

How many more turkey
sandwiches did the deli sell
than tuna sandwiches?   _____ sandwiches

Determine if the problem compares amounts.
Then circle the number sentence.

9. The snack stand sold 22 nacho snacks and
8 candy bars.

How many fewer candy bars did it sell than
nacho snacks?

Does this problem involve comparing two
amounts?

A. Yes   B. No

Which number sentence would solve this
problem?

A. $22 + 8 = ?$ B. $22 - 8 = ?$

10. Children bought 11 tickets. Adults bought 4 more tickets than children.

How many tickets did adults buy?

Does this problem involve comparing two amounts?

A. Yes   B. No

Which number sentence would solve this problem?

A. $11 + 4 = ?$ B. $11 - 4 = ?$

Circle Add or Subtract to tell how you would solve the problem. Then use base-10 blocks or sketches to solve.

1. Sierra had 26 dolls in her collection. She got 15 more dolls.

   How many dolls does Sierra have now?   _____ dolls

   A. Add   B. Subtract

2. Tony had 36 golf balls. He gave 16 golf balls to his sister.

   How many golf balls does Tony have left?   _____ golf balls

   A. Add   B. Subtract

Solve the problem. If needed, use base-10 blocks and a part-part-total chart to help you.

3. Max has 15 blue cups and 21 red cups.

   How many cups does he have in all?   _____ cups

4. Sari has 36 photos. 14 of the photos are of her friends.
The rest are of her family.

How many of Sari's photos are of her family?   _____ photos

5. The Rose Café had 54 chairs outside. They added some more. Now the café has 87 chairs outside.

How many chairs did the café add?   _____ chairs

Solve the problem. If needed, use a start-change-result chart to help you.

6. In the morning, there were 47 boxes of cereal on the shelf at the store.
At the end of the day, there were 20 boxes of cereal on the shelf.

How many boxes of cereal did people buy during the day?   _____ boxes

7. Jeff picked 23 red tomatoes.
Then he bought 12 more tomatoes.

How many tomatoes does Jeff have in all?   _____ tomatoes

Solve the problem. If needed, use base-10 blocks to help you.

8. The Pumas scored 16 points in the football game.
The Tigers scored 21 points in the football game.

How many fewer points did the Pumas score than the Tigers?

_____ fewer points

9. There are 23 pink flowers in a vase.
There are 5 more red flowers than pink flowers in the same vase.

How many red flowers are in the vase?

_____ flowers

10. A radio station played 45 songs in the morning.
It played 57 songs in the evening.

How many more songs did the station play in the evening than in the morning?

_____ songs

Draw a sketch to show how to solve the problem.

11. A tree had 34 oranges on it.
Later that day, a man picked 14 oranges
from the tree.

How many oranges are left on the tree?

_____ oranges left on the tree

Solve.

12. Circle which one is asking you to combine
two quantities and then solve that problem.

A. Pete had 65 stickers.
He gave 20 to his brother.

How many stickers does he have now?

B. Sylvie bought 65 stickers.
Josh bought 20 stickers.

How many stickers do they have altogether?

_____ stickers

Equalize Story Problems

Make the Numbers Equal

Draw jumps on the number line from one number to the other to model the story problem. First make jumps of 10 if you can. Then make jumps of 1. Then solve the story problem by counting the lengths of the jumps you made.

1. The bakery has already sold 57 cookies today. Yesterday the bakery sold 69 cookies.

   How many more cookies must the bakery sell today to sell the same number of cookies as it sold yesterday?

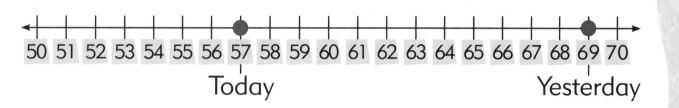

50 51 52 53 54 55 56 57 58 59 60 61 62 63 64 65 66 67 68 69 70

Today   Yesterday

$57 + \underline{\hspace{2cm}} = 69$

_____ cookies

TRY IT

2. Ava put 78 pennies into a piggy bank.
She put 58 pennies into a jar.

How many pennies must Ava take out of
the piggy bank to have the same number of
pennies in the piggy bank and the jar?

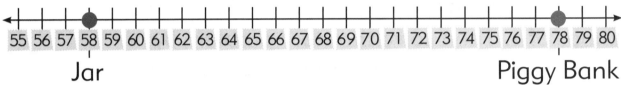

78 − 58 = _____

_____ pennies

---

3. Ryan read 34 pages.
Luke read 21 pages.

How many more pages must Luke read to have
read the same number of pages as Ryan?

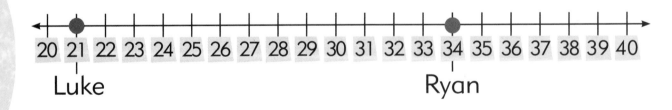

21 + _____ = 34

_____ pages

Solve the story problem. You may use a number line to help you.

4. Troy bought 88 stickers.
   Jonathan bought 53 stickers.
   How many more stickers does Jonathan need to buy to have as many stickers as Troy?

   _____ stickers

5. Eduardo has 17 books.
   Ron has 12 books.
   How many books does Ron have to buy to have as many books as Eduardo?

   _____ books

6. Susan collected 24 shells.
   Laura collected 77 shells.
   How many more shells does Susan have to collect to have the same number of shells as Laura?

   _____ shells

TRY IT

7. Claire has 6 peanuts.
   Susan has 2 peanuts.
   How many peanuts does Claire have to eat to have as many peanuts as Susan?

   _____ peanuts

8. Marie's necklace has 64 beads.
   Edna's necklace has 42 beads.
   How many beads must Marie take off her necklace to have the same number of beads as Edna?

   _____ beads

9. Ira has 15 plants.
   Helen has 39 plants.
   How many plants does Helen need to give away to have the same number of plants as Ira?

   _____ plants

Make Them Equal

Equal Amounts

Follow the directions to solve the story problem.

1. Jamie built a train with 16 cars. Bob built a train with 5 cars.

   How many more cars does Bob need to add to his train to have the same number as Jamie?

   Use a number line to mark the number of cars Jamie used and the number Bob used. Mark the line with a "J" for Jamie and a "B" for Bob.

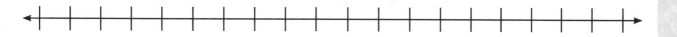

   To find out how many more Bob needs, jump by 10s then ones to move from 5 to 16.

   Then answer the question "How many more cars does Bob need to add to his train to have the same number of cars as Jamie?"

    cars

TRY IT

Circle the number sentence you could use to solve the problem.

2. Tom has 30 pencils.

If Tom gives away 10 pencils, he will have the same number of pencils as Frank.

How many pencils does Frank have?

A. $30 - 10 = 20$

B. $30 + 10 = 40$

C. $10 + 30 = 40$

Solve. You may use a number line to help you.

3. Kelly has 44 comic books and Fran has 10 comic books.

How many more comic books does Fran need to have the same number of comic books as Kelly?

_____ comic books

---

4. Joe has 45 hens and Pete has 12 hens.

How many hens does Joe need to give away to have the same number of hens as Pete?

_____ hens

5. Melinda has 54 marbles.
   If Melinda buys 25 more marbles, she will have the same number of marbles as Linda.

   How many marbles does Linda have?

   _____ marbles

6. Daryl scored 5 goals.
   If Daryl scores 3 more goals, he will have scored the same number of goals as Brandon.

   How many goals did Brandon score?

   _____ goals

7. Ron rode his bike 15 miles on Saturday.
   If Ron had ridden 22 more miles, he would have ridden the same number of miles as John.

   How many miles has John ridden?

   _____ miles

8. Beth baked 12 muffins.
If Beth gives away 5 muffins, she will have the same number of muffins as Jim.

How many muffins does Jim have?

_____ muffins

9. Barbara picked 54 apples.
If Barbara gives 23 apples away, she will have the same number of apples as Cathy.

How many apples does Cathy have?

_____ apples

10. Rich has 76 comic books.
If Rich gives away 24 comic books, he will have the same number of comic books as Chris.

How many comic books does Chris have?

_____ comic books

More Story Problems

Make Groups Equal

Use base-10 blocks and paper plates to solve.

1. A pet store has 93 guppies.
   If it sells 42 guppies, it will have the same number of guppies as angelfish.

   How many angelfish does the pet store have?

   _____ angelfish

2. The Cardinals brought 23 basketballs for their warm up.
   If the other team had 11 more basketballs, it would have same number of basketballs as the Cardinals.

   How many basketballs does the other team have?

   _____ basketballs

3. Mr. Lee has 44 hot dogs to sell.
   If he gets 14 more hot dogs, he will have the same number of hot dogs as hot dog buns.

   How many hot dog buns does Mr. Lee have?

   _____ buns

LEARN

4. One apartment building has 64 floors. Another apartment building being built has 33 floors so far.

How many more floors need to be built so that both buildings have the same number of floors?

_____ floors

Use a number line to solve.

5. Hannah has 12 marbles. Jacob has 18 marbles.

How many more marbles does Hannah need buy to have as many marbles as Jacob has?

_____ marbles

---

6. The grocery store has 55 apples. It also has 35 oranges.

How many apples does the grocery store need to sell to have the same number of apples as oranges?

_____ apples

7. The gardener planted 75 bushes in one area of the park.
She also planted 52 trees in another area of the park.

How many more trees does she need to plant to have the same number of trees as bushes?

_____ trees

8. The animal shelter has 28 dogs ready to be adopted.
It also has 15 cats.

How many dogs will have to be adopted so that the shelter has the same number of dogs as cats?

_____ dogs

More Story Problems

Practice Equalize Problems

Circle the answer.

1. The zoo has 5 pandas and 10 giraffes. The zoo has how many fewer pandas than giraffes?

   Does this problem involve making amounts equal?

   A. Yes   B. No

2. Tanya has 28 apples in her refrigerator. She also has 15 peaches.

   How many peaches will Tanya need to buy to have the same number of peaches as apples?

   Does this problem involve making amounts equal?

   A. Yes   B. No

TRY IT

3. Edward drew 11 pictures and Pete drew 7 pictures. How many pictures did they draw altogether?

Does this problem involve making amounts equal?

A. Yes

B. No

4. The zoo has 28 snakes. The zoo also has 39 frogs.

How many more snakes does the zoo need to get to have the same number of snakes as frogs?

Does this problem involve making amounts equal?

A. Yes

B. No

Solve.

5. Ken biked 17 miles. Jim biked 10 miles. How many more miles does Jim need to bike to travel the same distance as Ken?

_____ miles

6. Jackson made a house of cards with 28 cards. Makena made a house of cards with 20 cards.

How many cards should Jackson remove from his house to have the same number of cards as Makena?

_____ cards

7. Wendy picked 54 plums.
If she gives 24 plums away, she will have the same number of plums as Ben.

How many plums does Ben have?

_____ plums

8. Wade rode his bike 24 miles on Sunday.
If he had ridden 23 more miles, he would have ridden the same number of miles as Brad.

How many miles had Brad ridden?

_____ miles

Explore Number Sentences

Solve Problems with Number Sentences

Circle the number sentence that correctly solves the problem.

1. Amanda has 17 dresses. If she gives away 14 dresses, she will have the same number of dresses as Dana.

   How many dresses does Dana have?

   Which number sentence correctly solves this problem?

   A. $17 - 14 = 3$

   B. $14 - 17 = 3$

   C. $17 - 14 = 31$

2. Meg had 72 rocks in her collection. She gave 11 rocks to Paul.

   How many rocks does Meg have left?

   A. $11 - 72 = 61$

   B. $72 - 11 = 61$

   C. $72 + 11 = 83$

3. Brittney has 24 pink roses and 54 red roses.

How many roses does she have altogether?

A. $54 - 24 = 30$

B. $24 - 54 = 30$

C. $24 + 54 = 78$

---

4. The Panthers scored 26 points in the football game. The Tigers scored 37 points in the football game.

How many fewer points did the Panthers score than the Tigers?

A. $26 + 37 = 63$

B. $26 - 37 = 11$

C. $37 - 26 = 11$

Solve.

5. Matthew brought 24 sandwiches to a party. Maria brought 32 sandwiches.

How many sandwiches did they bring altogether?

_____ sandwiches

TRY IT

Number Sentences

Story Problems with Number Sentences

Circle the number sentence that solves the problem.

1. Jack has 23 comic books. If Jack gets 9 more comic books, then he will have the same number of comic books as Hannah. How many comic books does Hannah have?

   A. $23 - 9 = 14$

   B. $23 + 9 = 32$

   C. $32 + 9 = 41$

2. George has 7 fewer toy trucks than Andrew. Andrew has 39 toy trucks. How many toy trucks does George have?

   A. $39 - 7 = 32$

   B. $39 + 7 = 46$

   C. $46 - 7 = 29$

3. Some ducks are swimming in a pond. 14 ducks fly away. There are 25 ducks left in the pond. How many ducks were in the pond at the beginning?

   A. $25 + 14 = 39$

   B. $14 + 11 = 25$

   C. $25 - 14 = 11$

TRY IT

Write a number sentence and solve the problem.

4. Carol has 9 stickers. If Carol gets 3 more stickers, she will have the same number of stickers as Ron. How many stickers does Ron have?

   _____ ◯ _____ = ?   _____ stickers

5. Roger picked 6 more apples than Andrew. Andrew picked 4 apples. How many apples did Roger pick?

   _____ ◯ _____ = ?   _____ apples

6. Some children were playing in the park. 8 children went home. There are now 13 children playing in the park. How many children were playing in the park at the beginning?

   ? ◯ _____ = _____   _____ children

Circle the number sentence that solves the problem.

7. Bobby has 22 grapes. If he gives away 12 grapes, he will have the same number of grapes as Carlos. How many grapes does Carlos have?

   A. $22 - 12 = 10$

   B. $12 - 22 = 10$

   C. $22 + 12 = 34$

8. Ashley has 46 stickers. If she gives away 23 stickers, she will have the same number of stickers as her sister. How many stickers does her sister have?

A. $46 + 23 = 69$

B. $46 - 23 = 23$

C. $23 - 46 = 23$

9. Ricky sold 38 comics. Tim sold 49 comics. How many more comics must Ricky sell to have sold as many comics as Tim?

A. $38 - 49 = 11$

B. $38 + 49 = 87$

C. $49 - 38 = 11$

10. Sam ran 46 laps around the track. Miley ran 2 more laps than Sam. How many laps did Miley run around the track?

A. $46 - 2 = 44$

B. $2 - 46 = 44$

C. $46 + 2 = 48$

TRY IT

11. Tim had 38 cards. His dad gave him some more cards. Now Tim has 69 cards. How many cards did Tim's dad give him?

A. $38 + 69 = 107$

B. $69 - 38 = 31$

C. $69 - 38 = 21$

12. Polly had 55 dimes. Her mom gave her some more dimes. Now Polly has 67 dimes. How many dimes did Polly's mom give her?

A. $67 - 55 = 12$

B. $55 + 67 = 122$

C. $55 - 67 = 12$

Write and Solve Number Sentences

Write and Solve Sentences

Think about what is happening in the story.
Then write and solve a number sentence to
find the answer to the question.

1. Trent has 56 books.
   He has some on bookshelves and some in a box.
   There are 14 books in the box.

   How many books are on the bookshelves?

   Number sentence that explains what's happening
   in the problem:

   _____

   Number sentence you will solve:

   _____

   Trent has _____ books on the bookshelves.

2. Brad's team scored 16 points.
His team scored 7 fewer points than
Tammy's team.

How many points did Tammy's team score?

Number sentence that explains what's happening
in the problem:

_____

Number sentence you will solve:

_____

Tammy's team scored _____ points.

---

3. Ian collected some seashells at the beach.
He gave 6 seashells to Val.
He now has 14 seashells.

How many seashells did Ian collect?

Number sentence that explains what's happening
in the problem:

_____

Number sentence you will solve:

_____

Ian collected _____ seashells.

4. Brianna used 24 stickers to decorate her notebook. If she uses 15 more stickers, then she'll have used a full sheet of stickers.

How many stickers are on a full sheet?

Number sentence that explains what's happening in the problem:

_____

Number sentence you will solve:

_____

_____ stickers are on a full sheet.

5. The pet store has turtles and frogs.
It has 6 turtles.
There are 8 more frogs than turtles.

How many frogs does the pet store have?

Number sentence that explains what's happening in the problem:

_____

Number sentence you will solve:

_____

The pet store has _____ frogs.

6. The toy store has 17 scooters and some bicycles. If the store sells 5 scooters, it will have the same number of scooters as bicycles.

How many bicycles does the store have?

Number sentence that explains what's happening in the problem:

_____

Number sentence you will solve:

_____

The store has _____ bicycles.

Write and Solve Number Sentences

Solve Story Problems

Write the number sentences asked for in the question and answer the question.

1. Larry ran 49 laps. He ran some laps on Thursday and some on Friday.
   Larry ran 19 laps on Thursday.
   How many laps did Larry run on Friday?

   Number sentence that explains
   what's happening in the problem: _____

   Number sentence you will solve: _____

   Larry ran _____ laps on Friday.

2. Emily collected 38 seashells.
   She collected 9 fewer seashells than Peter.
   How many seashells did Peter collect?

   Number sentence that explains
   what's happening in the problem: _____

   Number sentence you will solve: _____

   Peter collected _____ seashells.

T R Y   I T

3. Mark gave 4 of his coins away. Mark now has 21 coins. How many coins did he have at the start?

Number sentence that explains what's happening in the problem: _____

Number sentence you will solve: _____

Mark had _____ coins at the start.

4. The fruit stand has 59 red apples and some green apples. If the stand sells 14 red apples, it will have the same number of red apples as green apples. How many green apples does the stand have?

Number sentence that explains what's happening in the problem: _____

Number sentence you will solve: _____

The stand has _____ green apples.

Circle the number sentence that shows how to solve the problem.

5. Tom ate 26 carrot sticks last week and 12 carrot sticks this week. How many carrot sticks did Tom eat altogether?

A. $26 - 12 = 14$

B. $12 - 26 = 14$

C. $26 + 12 = 38$

6. There were 14 gophers on the grass. 9 gophers went into a hole. How many gophers are left on the grass?

A. $14 + 9 = 23$

B. $14 - 9 = 5$

C. $9 - 14 = 5$

Check Your Answers

Answer Check

Check the answer to the problem.
Tell how you checked it.

1. Ed solved this story problem:

   Al has 17 toy cars. He has 11 toy trucks.
   How many more toy cars does Al have than
   toy trucks?

   Ed's answer:
   $17 - 11 = 5$
   Al has 5 more toy cars than trucks.

   Check Ed's answer.

   Is it correct or incorrect?

   How do you know?

   _____

   _____

   _____

   If incorrect solve:

   _____

   Al has _____ more toy cars than trucks.

TRY IT

2. Jennifer solved this story problem:

Ana has 16 dolls in her collection.
She gives 4 away to her sister.
How many dolls does Ana have left?

Jennifer's answer:
$16 + 4 = 20$
20 dolls are left.

Check Jennifer's answer.

Is it correct or incorrect?

How do you know?

_____

_____

_____

_____

_____

If incorrect solve:

_____

Ana had _____ dolls left.

3. Pete solved this story problem:

Eric wants to run 45 laps at the track.
He has run 23 laps already.
How many laps does Eric have left to run?

Pete's answer:
$45 - 23 = 22$

Eric has 22 laps left to run.

Check Pete's answer.

Is it correct or incorrect?

How do you know?

_____

_____

If incorrect solve:

_____

Eric has _____ more laps to run.

Solve the problem and then check the solution using another method you have learned.

4. Bill had 23 blocks in the box.
He gave 12 blocks to Amy.

How many blocks does Bill have left?

_____

_____

TRY IT

Circle the answer to the problem.

5. Sam solved this story problem:

   Dee saved 12 pennies. Paul saved 29 pennies. How many pennies did they save in all?

   Sam's answer: $12 + 29 = 41$ pennies

   Which number sentence could you use to check Sam's work?

   A. $12 + 41 = 52$

   B. $41 - 12 = 29$

   C. $41 + 29 = 70$

---

6. Which problem is solved correctly?

   A. Maria has 26 stickers. She bought 9 more. How many stickers does Maria have altogether?

      Answer: 36 stickers

   B. Michael has 14 games. He has 27 books. How many more books than games does Michael have?

      Answer: 41 more books

   C. Joe had 35 baseball cards. He gave 23 to his brother. How many baseball cards does Joe have now?

      Answer: 12 baseball cards

Explain Solution Strategies

Model or Sketch to Solve

Use sketches or base-10 blocks to solve.

1. There were 73 flags in a park.
   The veterans place 22 more flags.

   How many flags are in the park now?

   _____ flags

2. The jar had 38 peanuts and 26 almonds.

   How many more peanuts were in the jar
   than almonds?

   _____ more peanuts

3. Mr. Mead's class read 29 books.
   Ms. Little's class read 16 books.

   How many more books does Ms. Little's
   class need to read to have read as many
   books as Mr. Mead's class?

   _____ more books

LEARN

4. Children bought 64 cups of apple juice at the snack stand.

They bought 35 cups of grape juice.

How many cups of juice did children buy altogether?

_____ cups of juice

Explain Solution Strategies

Explain How to Solve

Circle the answer that explains the correct way to solve the problem.

1. Jeff had 28 books.
    Matt had 32 books.

    How many books do they have altogether?

    A. Add 28 and 32 because the problem asks for how many books they have altogether.

    B. Subtract 28 from 32 because the problem asks to compare Matt's books to Jeff's.

2. Jeff had 28 books.
    Jeff bought 5 more books.

    How many books does Jeff have now?

    A. Add 28 and 5 because the problem asks about a change in the number of books Jeff has after buying 5 more books.

    B. Subtract 5 from 28 because Jeff gets rid of some books.

T R Y   I T

3. Jeff had 28 books.
   Matt had 32 books.

   How many more books does Matt have than Jeff?

   A. Add 28 and 32 to find how many books Matt and Jeff have.

   B. Subtract 28 from 32 because the problem asks to find how many more books Matt has then Jeff.

4. Jeff has 28 books.
   Matt has 32 books.

   How many books does Jeff need to buy to have as many books as Matt?

   A. Add 28 and 32 to find how many books Matt and Jeff have.

   B. Subtract 28 from 32 because the problem asks how many Jeff needs to have the same number as Matt.

Circle the answer. You may use base-10 blocks to help you.

5. Carl threw 51 pitches in the baseball game. Tony threw 31 pitches.

How many pitches did they throw altogether?

To solve this problem, Joey used this number sentence: $51 + 31 = 82$.

Did Joey correctly solve this problem?

A. No, because you have to use subtraction to find the difference between the two numbers of pitches.

B. Yes, because you need to add the two numbers together to find out the total number of pitches.

C. Yes, because you need to add the two numbers together to find the difference between the two numbers of pitches.

TRY IT

6. Which best explains how to correctly solve this problem?

Cash just got 8 new pond snails for his fish tank.
He already had 25 pond snails.
How many pond snails does Cash have now?

A. $25 + 8$, because Cash has 8 more snails than when he started.

B. $25 - 8$, because Cash has 8 fewer snails than when he started.

C. $25 + 8$, because Cash has 8 fewer snails than when he started.

7. Which best explains how to correctly solve this problem?

Jasmine has 11 cookies.
If Jasmine gives away 7 cookies, she will have the same number of cookies as Casey.
How many cookies does Casey have?

A. Add 11 and 7 to find out how many cookies there are altogether.

B. Subtract 7 from 11 to find out how many cookies Casey has.

C. Add 11 and 7 to find out how many cookies Casey has.

TRY IT

8. Which best explains how to correctly solve this problem?

Callie painted 34 tiles.
Alice painted 28 tiles.
How many fewer tiles did Alice paint than Callie?

A. $34 + 28$, because Alice and Callie painted 62 tiles altogether.

B. $28 - 34$, because Alice painted fewer tiles than Callie.

C. $34 - 28$, because Alice painted fewer tiles than Callie.

---

9. Which best explains how to correctly solve this problem?

Simon picked 17 apples and Anna picked 12 apples.
How many more apples did Simon pick than Anna?

A. $12 - 17$, because Anna picked more apples than Simon.

B. $17 - 12$, because Simon picked more apples than Anna.

C. $17 + 12$, because Simon picked more apples than Anna.

TRY IT

Justify Selected Procedures

Use a Number Sentence to Solve

Circle the answer.

1. Rich used the number sentence $26 + 53 = ?$ to solve this problem:

   Carly had 53 flowers.
   She picked 26 more flowers.
   How many flowers does Carly have now?

   Is Rich correct?

   A. Yes   B. No

2. David used the number sentence $75 - 23 = ?$ to solve this problem:

   Cathy has 75 stickers. Chad has 23 stickers. How many more stickers does Cathy have than Chad?

   Is David correct?

   A. Yes   B. No

TRY IT

Decide if the number sentence will solve the problem, and tell why or why not.

3. Lisa used the number sentence $45 + 21 = ?$ to solve this problem:

The bakery made 45 muffins.
21 are apple and the rest are blueberry.
How many muffins are blueberry?

Is Lisa correct? Explain your answer.

_____

4. Raul used the number sentence $25 - 62 = ?$ to solve this problem:

Rhonda has 25 books.
Lucy has 62 books.
How many fewer books does Rhonda have than Lucy?

Is Raul correct? Explain your answer.

_____

5. Jonathan used the number sentence $41 - 9 = ?$ to solve this problem:

Becky had 41 toy cars.
She gave 9 to her sister.
How many toy cars does Becky have now?

Is Jonathan correct? Explain your answer.

_____

Justify Different Solutions

Explain the Solution

Cut out the strips and fold them in half.
Explain how you would solve each problem and
explain why. Then check your answer.

---

1. On Monday, the ice show sold 67 tickets online.
   So far today, the show has sold 43 tickets online.

   How many more tickets does the show need to sell online today to equal the number of tickets sold on Monday?

   | I'm trying to make two amounts equal. I know that 67 is the number I need to reach. I can think of this as, "43 + a missing number is 67."

   $43 + ? = 67$

   I can find the missing number by solving the fact family number sentence $67 - 43 = ?$

---

2. At the start of the show, 18 boys skated onto the ice.
   Then 9 girls join them.

   How many skaters are on the ice now?

   | I know that there are 18 boys at the start and that amount changes when 9 girls join them. Since there are more skaters now, I will add.

   $18 + 9 = ?$

---

3. The usher had some programs.
   She got 63 more to hand out and now she has 95.

   How many programs did she have at the beginning?

   | I don't know how many programs the usher had at the start, but when she got more, she had 95. Since she got 63 more, I need to add 63 to a missing amount to make 95.

   $? + 63 = 95$

   I can find the missing number by solving the fact family number sentence $95 - 63 = ?$

---

4. Luke ate 32 raisins during the show.
   Marcy ate 44 raisins.

   How many fewer raisins did Luke eat than Marcy?

   | In this problem, I need to compare Luke's amount to Marcy's to see how many fewer raisins Luke ate. I need to find the difference, so I will subtract.

   $44 - 32 = ?$

---

5. During one act, 45 skaters were on the ice.
   Then 23 skated off.

   How many skaters were left on the ice?

   | In this problem, 45 skaters were on the ice. The 23 that skated off would be taken away from the 45, so I'll subtract.

   $45 - 23 = ?$

LEARN

Justify Different Solutions

Justify Solutions

Read the story problem. Circle Add or Subtract to show how you would solve the problem, and then tell why you would add or subtract.

1. Mike took 85 photos.
   Jake took 32 photos.

   How many more photos did Mike take than Jake?

   A. Add   B. Subtract

2. The circus sold 98 tickets on Saturday. On Sunday morning, it sold 61 tickets.

   How many more tickets does the circus need to sell on Sunday to equal the number of tickets sold on Saturday?

   A. Add   B. Subtract

TRY IT

3. Sally had 75 programs.
She gave out 43 programs.

How many programs are left?

A. Add   B. Subtract

4. The snack shack sold 56 lemon ice drinks.
It sold 22 strawberry ice drinks.

How many ice drinks did the snack shack
sell altogether?

A. Add   B. Subtract

Read the problem and follow the directions.

5. Heidi had 24 pencil erasers.
Her mom buys her 7 new erasers.
How many pencil erasers does Heidi have now?

What is a correct way to solve this problem?

Explain why you would solve it that way.

6. Olivia has 49 barrettes.
18 barrettes are rectangle shaped.
The rest of the barrettes are square.
How many square barrettes does Olivia have?

What is a correct way to solve this problem?

Explain why you would solve it that way.

---

7. Chase used 45 gallons of water to wash his truck.
Annie used 33 gallons of water to wash her truck.
How many fewer gallons of water did Annie
use than Chase?

What is a correct way to solve this problem?

Explain why you would solve it that way.

Circle the answer.

8. Justine has 35 raisins.
   Michelle has 31 raisins.
   How many more raisins does Justine have than Michelle?

   Which expression could be used to solve this problem?

   Why is this expression used?

   A. 35 − 31, because you subtract to find the difference in the number of raisins Justine and Michelle have.

   B. 35 + 31, because you add find how many raisins they have altogether.

   C. 31 − 35, because you subtract to find how many more raisins Justine has.

Name:

Read the problem and follow the directions.

1. Read the story problems. Tell how you can use Problem 1 to help you solve Problem 2. Then solve Problem 2.

Problem 1

Heather has 59 stuffed animals.
Ellen has 8 stuffed animals.

How many fewer stuffed animals does Ellen have than Heather?

$59 - 8 = 51$

Problem 2

There are 39 apples.
There are 7 oranges.

How many more apples are there than oranges?

_____

TRY IT

2. Write a number sentence and solution for Problem 1. Then use that number sentence and solution to help you solve Problem 2.

Problem 1

There are 36 boys at the park.

There are 8 girls at the park.

How many children are at the park altogether?

_____   _____ children

Problem 2

There are 15 brown bears and 5 black bears at the zoo.

How many bears are there in all?

_____   _____ bears

What is alike about Problem 1 and Problem 2? Circle the answer.

| Both are solved with subtraction. | Both are solved with addition. |

3. Use the solution to Problem 1 to help you solve Problem 2.

Problem 1

There are 22 peanut butter and 5 turkey sandwiches.

How many sandwiches are there altogether?

$22 + 5 = 27$

Problem 2

There are 34 goldfish.
9 goldfish join them.

How many goldfish are there in all?

_____

What is alike about Problem 1 and Problem 2? Circle the answer.

Both are solved with subtraction.

Both are solved with addition.

TRY IT

4. Use the solution to Problem 1 to help you solve Problem 2.

Problem 1

Ted had 17 seashells.

He gave 5 seashells to his brother.

How many seashells does Ted have now?

$17 - 5 = 12$

Problem 2

Anne's book has 79 pages.
She read 9 pages.

How many pages does Anne have left to read?

_____

What is alike about Problem 1 and Problem 2?
Circle the answer.

Both are solved with subtraction.

Both are solved with addition.

TRY IT

Write Story Problems

Create Story Problems

You can use the given number sentence to solve the story problem. Create a different story problem that you can solve by using the same number sentence.

1. $14 - 7 = 7$

There were 14 birds in the field.
Seven birds flew away.
How many birds are left?

_____

_____

_____

2. $6 + 9 = 15$

Alexander picked 6 apples.
Winnie picked 9 apples.
How many apples did they pick in all?

_____

_____

_____

LEARN

3. $12 - 8 = 4$

Serena had 12 books. She gave 8 books to the library. How many books does Serena have now?

_____

_____

4. $3 + 5 - 4 = ?$

John made 3 cookies and Rosa made 5 cookies. They put the cookies together and gave 4 to Winnie. How many cookies do John and Rosa have now?

_____

_____

_____

Create two story problems that can be solved by using the number sentence.

5. $3 + 4 = ?$

_____

_____

6. $18 - 4 = ?$

_____

_____

Write Story Problems

Matching Story Problems

You can use the given number sentence to solve the story problem. Create a different story problem that you can solve by using the same number sentence.

1. $20 - 1 = 19$

There were 20 muffins in the box.
Kim took 1 muffin.

How many muffins are left in the box?

_____

_____

_____

2. $11 + 15 = 26$

There are 11 boys and 15 girls
in the class.

How many students are in the class?

_____

_____

_____

TRY IT

3. $8 - 5 + 2 = ?$

Lynn had 8 stickers. She gave 5 stickers to Betsy. Then Mandy gave Lynn 2 more stickers.

How many stickers does Lynn have now?

_____

_____

_____

_____

Create a story problem that can be solved by using the number sentence.

4. $8 + 4 = ?$

_____

_____

_____

_____

5. $10 - 5 = ?$

_____

_____

_____

_____

Create two story problems that can be solved
by using the number sentence.

6. $2 + 9 = ?$

_____

_____

_____

_____

TRY IT

Circle the number sentence you could use to solve the problem.

7. Anne had 6 toy cars.
She lost 3 toy cars.

How many cars does she have now?

   A. $6 - 3 = ?$

   B. $6 + 3 = ?$

   C. $6 + 1 = ?$

---

8. Sasha had 7 doll dresses.
Then she gave 2 doll dresses to her friend.

How many doll dresses does Sasha have left?

   A. $7 + 2 = ?$

   B. $2 + 7 = ?$

   C. $7 - 2 = ?$

TRY IT

Unit Review

Checkpoint Practice

Write a number sentence that shows what's happening in the problem. Then solve the number sentence.

1. There were 12 birds in the tree.
    5 birds flew away.

    How many birds will be left in the tree?

    Number sentence: _____

    Answer: _____ birds

Check the problem. Tell how you checked it.

2. Johnny solved this story problem:

    Lucas has 19 crayons.
    11 of these crayons are red.

    How many crayons are not red?

    Johnny's answer: $19 - 11 = 8$
    There are 8 crayons that are not red.

    A. Correct   B. Incorrect

    How do you know?

    If incorrect, solve.

Read the two problems. Tell how Problem 1 is like Problem 2. Then use the way Problem 1 was solved to help you solve Problem 2.

3. **Problem 1**

Brandon ran for 42 minutes and then stopped for a glass of water.
Then he ran for 15 more minutes.

How long did Brandon run?

Number sentence: $42 + 15 = 57$

Answer: Brandon ran for 57 minutes.

Problem 2

Joanna had 52 colored markers.
She bought 9 more.

How many markers does Joanna have now?

Number sentence: _____

Answer: _____

Circle the answer.

4. Max has 8 dogs.

Ruby has 2 more dogs than Max.

How many dogs does Ruby have?

Which of the following best explains how to correctly solve this problem?

  A. $8 + 2$, because Ruby has 2 more dogs than Max.

  B. $2 - 8$, because Ruby has 8 fewer dogs than Max.

  C. $8 - 2$, because Ruby has 2 more dogs than Max.

---

5. Which story problem can be solved using the number sentence $21 + 15 = ?$

  A. Martha has 21 stickers. Blake has 15 more stickers than Martha. How many stickers does Blake have?

  B. Jacob has 21 rocks. Aaron has 15 rocks. How many more rocks does Jacob have than Aaron?

  C. Danica has 21 seashells. Helio has 15 seashells. How many more seashells does Helio have to find to have as many as Danica?

6. Sandro washed 26 cars.
Toby washed 8 cars.

How many more cars does Toby need to wash to have washed the same number as Sandro?

A. 34

B. 26

C. 18

D. 8

Plane Figures

Plane Shapes

Write the number of sides and corners for the shape.

1.

_____ sides

_____ corners

2.

_____ sides

_____ corners

Circle the name of the shape of the face of the figure.

3.

A. square

B. circle

C. triangle

4.

A. square

B. circle

C. triangle

TRY IT

Write the name of the shape.

5.

_____

6.

_____

Say how the shapes are the same and how they are different.

7.

8.

9. How many sides does a square have?

A. 1

B. 2

C. 3

D. 4

---

10. What is the shape of this piece of paper?

A. circle

B. triangle

C. square

D. rectangle

11. What shape is this?

A. square

B. triangle

C. rectangle

D. oval

---

12. What is the same about these shapes?

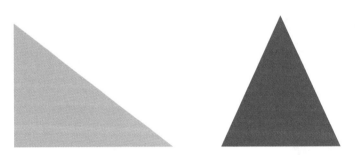

A. They both are triangles.

B. They both are squares.

C. They both have 4 corners.

D. They both have 4 sides.

Put Together and Take Apart Shapes

Practice Using Shapes

Use your blocks. Put together the triangles
to make the larger shape.

	Shapes	New Shape
1.		
2.		

Put together blocks to make the shape.
You may use any blocks.

3. 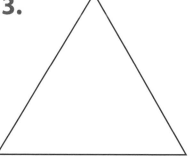 **4.**  **5.**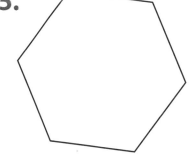

TRY IT

Draw a line or lines to show how to break the large shape into the smaller shapes that you are given in the problems.

6. 1 square and 1 triangle

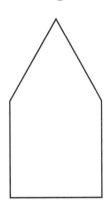

7. 1 square and 2 triangles

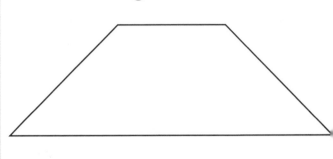

Draw a line or lines to show how to break the shape into smaller shapes like your blocks.

8.

9.

10.

Group Shapes Different Ways

Practice Sorting Shapes

Explain how the groups are sorted.
Say your answer.

1.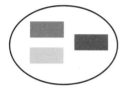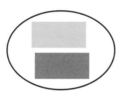

2.

3.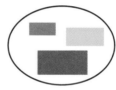

4.

Explain why the objects have been grouped together.
Say your answer.

5.

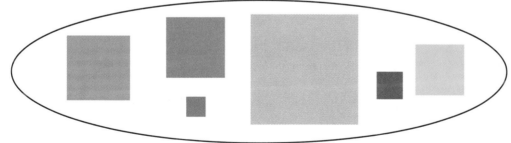

T R Y   I T

6.

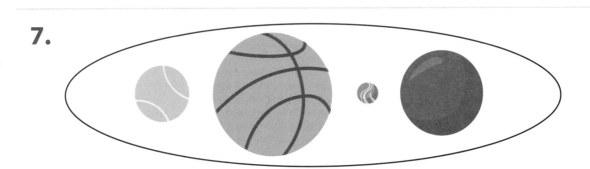

7.

Circle the answer.

8. Which shape belongs in this group?

A.

B.

C.

9. Why are the shapes grouped like this?

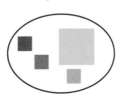

A. same size   B. same position   C. same color

Classify Objects and Data

Sort and Name

Sort the objects into 2 groups. Circle the objects that belong in 1 group. Cross out the objects that belong in the other group.

1.

2.

3.

67   18   81

99   38   20

59   2

TRY IT

Write a label for each group.

4.

_____   _____   _____

5.

_____   _____   _____

6.

10
70   90
40   30

13   71
52
66   93

_____   _____

TRY IT

Read the problem and follow the directions.

7. Sort the triangles into 2 groups.
Color one group green and the other group blue.

8. Circle the numbers that are less than 50.
Cross out the numbers that are greater than 50.

65   3   42   51   39

       21   7

    92   18

83   71   79

TRY IT

9. Circle the numbers that are less than 20. Draw a line under the numbers that are greater than 20.

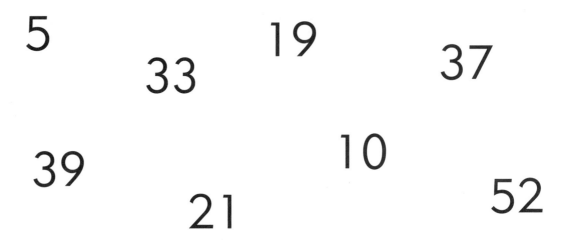

5   33   19   37

39   10   52

21

Circle the answer.

10. Why have these objects been grouped together?

A. All are the same size.

B. All are the same shape.

C. All are in the same position.

D. All are the same color.

11. Why have these numbers been grouped together?

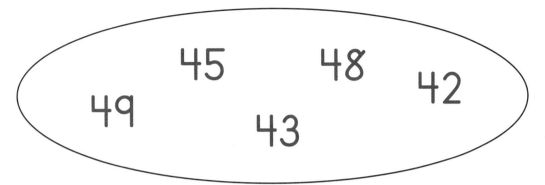

45   48
49   42
    43

A. All have the same ones digit.

B. All have the same tens digit.

C. All have three digits.

12. Why are the tissue box and shoe box in one group and the orange and tennis ball in another group?

A. Both are the same size.

B. Both are the same shape.

C. Both are the same color.

D. Both are in the same position.

13. Why have these objects been grouped together?

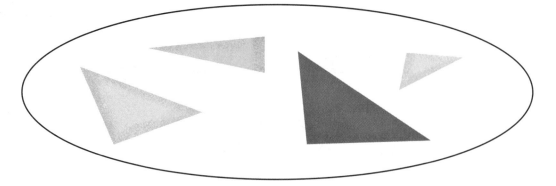

A. All are the same size.

B. All are the same shape.

C. All are in the same position.

D. All are the same color.

14. Why have these objects been grouped together?

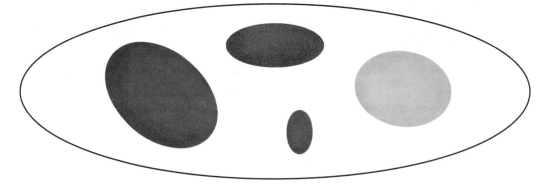

A. All are the same size.

B. All are the same shape.

C. All are in the same position.

D. All are the same color.

Identify and Extend Patterns

Draw the next 3 objects in the pattern.

1.

| 2 | 3 | 2 | 2 | 3 | 2 | 2 | 3 | 2 | 2 |

_____

2.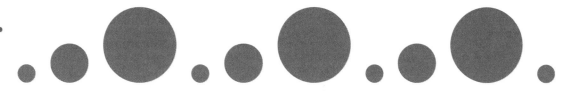

_____

3.

_____

TRY IT

Draw the next 3 objects in the pattern.
Explain how you got your answer.

4.  ____ ____ ____

_____

Circle the answer.

5. What are the next 3 shapes in this pattern?

⭐●■⭐●■⭐●■ ____ ____ ____

A. ●●●

B. ●⭐⭐

C. ■●⭐

D. ⭐●■

6. What are the next 4 colors in this pattern?

 ____ ____ ____ ____

A. ■■■■

B. ■■■■

C. ■■■■

D. ■■■■

7. What is the next number in this pattern?

$$2, 5, 6, 2, 5, 6, 2, 5, 6, \underline{}$$

A. 2   B. 5   C. 6

TRY IT

Tally Charts and Bar Graphs

Data in Charts and Graphs

Make a tally chart to show the number of coins Kevin has.

1. Kevin has 7 pennies, 2 nickels, 5 dimes, and 3 quarters in his pocket.

Kevin's Coins	

Use the Favorite Berries tally chart for Problems 2–4.

2. Which kind of berry did students pick the most?

_____

3. Which kind of berry did students pick the least?

_____

4. How many students picked blueberries?

_____

Favorite Berries	
strawberries 🍓	卌
raspberries	||||
blueberries ⬤	卌 |

TRY IT

Use the Pets bar graph for Problems 5–7.

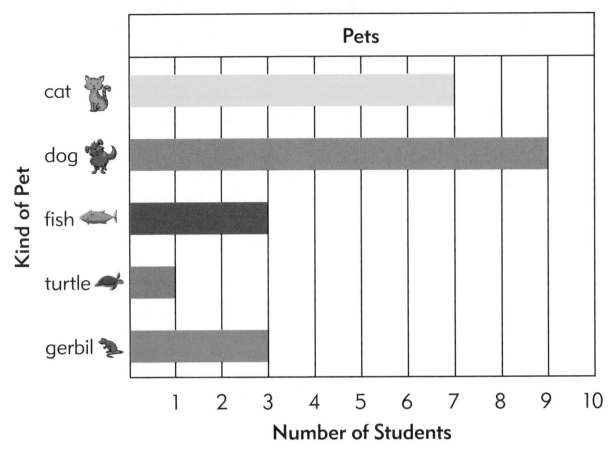

5. The least number of students have a _____.

6. The greatest number of students have a _____.

7. The same number of students have _____

and _____.

TRY IT

Read the problem and follow the directions.

8. Make a tally chart to show how many of each bear.

Bears	
🧸	
🧸	
🧸	

9. Robert looked at his list of chores.

He has to do 3 chores on Tuesdays, 7 chores on Wednesdays, and 2 chores on Thursdays.

Make a tally chart to show how many chores Robert has to do on these days.

Robert's Chores	
Tuesday	
Wednesday	
Thursday	

10. This tally chart shows the types of books Claire has.

Which type of book does Claire have the fewest of?

Circle the answer.

A. animals

B. plants

C. people

D. cartoons

Claire's Books	
animals	̶|̶|̶|̶|̶ ||||
plants	||
people	̶|̶|̶|̶|̶
cartoons	̶|̶|̶|̶|̶	

11. Look at the bar graph.

Keisha likes to count the birds in the park.

On which day did she count the most birds?

_____

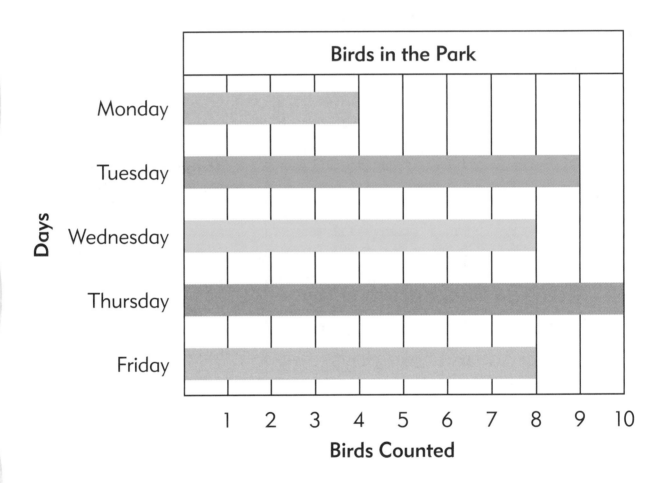

Birds in the Park

Days	
Monday	
Tuesday	
Wednesday	
Thursday	
Friday	

1 2 3 4 5 6 7 8 9 10

Birds Counted

TRY IT

Data in Pictures and Graphs

Share and Compare Data

Make a sketch to show your answer.
Then answer the question.

1. There are 4 ducks and 3 frogs in the pond
   Draw pictures to show how many of each
   animal are in the pond.

   Which shows more, the pictures
   of the ducks or the frogs? _____

2. Kendra has 5 pencils, 2 pens, and
   3 erasers in her pencil box. Make a picture
   to show how many of each item are in
   Kendra's pencil box.

   Which shows the fewest? _____

TRY IT

Violet took a picture to show how many of each type of sand toy she has. Use the picture to complete the sentence.

3. Violet has the fewest _____.

4. Violet has the most _____.

Make the graph. Then complete the sentence.

5. Jose made 4 chocolate cupcakes, 2 strawberry cupcakes, and 3 vanilla cupcakes. Make a picture graph to show how many of each type of cupcake Jose made.

Jose's Cupcakes							
Chocolate							
Strawberry							
Vanilla							

Each picture in the boxes equals 1.

6. Jose made the most _____ cupcakes.

TRY IT

Make the graph. Then complete the sentence.

7. A gym has 5 basketballs, 2 footballs, 8 jump ropes, and 5 flying disks. Make a picture graph to show how many of each toy is in the gym.

Gym Toys			

_____ _____ _____ _____

Each picture in the boxes equals 1.

8. The gym has the same number of _____

and _____ .

9. The gym has more _____ than any other toy.

TRY IT

Say the name of the shape.

1.

2.

3.

Say the answer.

4. What is different about these shapes?

5. Why have these objects been grouped together?

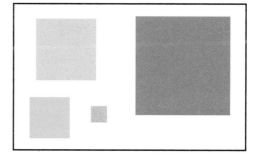

6. Peter is helping his mother get ready to wash clothes.

Which type of clothes do they have the most to wash?

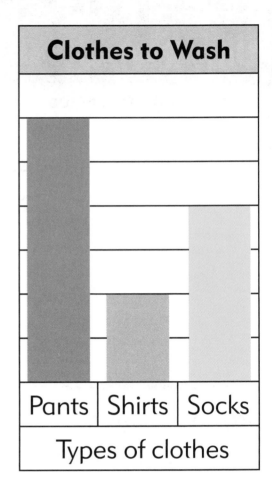

Clothes to Wash

Pants | Shirts | Socks

Types of clothes

Draw a line or lines on the shape to show how you could take it apart to make other shapes.

7.

8.

Read the problem and follow the directions.

9. Draw the next 3 objects in the pattern.

_____

10. Sort the objects into 2 groups. Circle the objects that belong in 1 group. Draw a box around the objects that belong in the other group.

11. Put 2 triangle blocks (F) together to make a square.

12. Jen went on a hike. She picked up 1 stick, 6 acorns, 4 leaves, and 3 flowers.

Make a picture graph to show the items Jen collected.

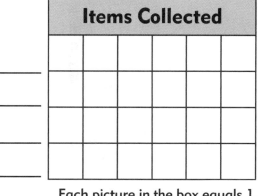

Items Collected

Each picture in the box equals 1.

13. Sort the sizes of the squares by coloring them. Color a group red, another group green, and the other group blue.

14. Carter has 5 bears, 3 rabbits, 7 dogs, and 1 cat in his stuffed animal collection. Make a tally chart to show the stuffed animals in Carter's collection.

Stuffed Animals	
Bears	
Rabbits	
Dogs	
Cats	

Circle the answer.

15. Circle the shape that belongs in the group. Tell why.

A.

B.

C.

16. Max saw 5 mice and 3 birds at the pet store. Which picture could Max draw to show how many mice and birds he saw?

A.

B.

C.

D.

17. This graph shows the hats that were sold at a yard sale. Which color of hat was sold most often?

Hats Sold at the Yard Sale	
Red hats	🎅🎅🎅🎅🎅🎅🎅
Green hats	🎅🎅🎅🎅🎅
Blue hats	🎅🎅🎅🎅🎅🎅🎅🎅🎅🎅
Yellow hats	🎅🎅🎅🎅🎅
Each 🎅 = 1 hat	

A. red   B. green   C. blue   D. yellow

Read the problem and follow the directions.

1. This diagram uses addition to show 6. Draw a subtraction diagram to show 6.

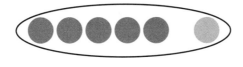

2. The answer to 5 − 3 is 2. Write 3 other expressions that have the answer 2.

_____

_____

_____

3. Why have these items been grouped together?

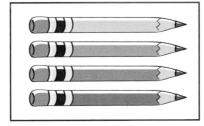 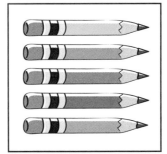

_____

4. Use the base-10 blocks to show the number 43.

5. Use paper clips to measure the length of a pencil and a crayon.

About how many paper clips long is the pencil? _____ paper clips

About how many paper clips long is the crayon? _____ paper clips

How much longer is the pencil than the crayon in paper clips? _____ paper clips

6. Look at the tally chart. Who ate the fewest hot dogs?

_____ ate the fewest hot dogs.

Hot Dogs Eaten	
Jack	I
Steven	IIII
Kenta	III
Julio	II

Draw a sketch to show how to solve. Then answer the question.

7. Tony was making a bracelet using red and blue beads. First he put 41 red beads on the string and then he put 13 blue beads on the string. How many beads did Tony use?

_____ beads

8. There were 29 fish in a tank. 6 of those fish were sold. How many fish were left in the tank?

_____ fish

Solve.

9. Toby has 42 trains. 10 of them are black and the rest are red. How many trains are red?

_____

10. Tom ate 7 cookies with milk. Ben ate 12 cookies with milk. How many more cookies did Ben eat than Tom? _____

Circle the answer.

11. This pinecone is about how many paper clips long?

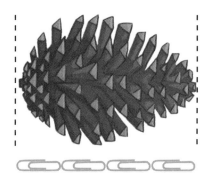

A. 3

B. 4

C. 7

D. 9

12. Some children used a balance and some coins to compare some objects. Which object weighed the most?

A.
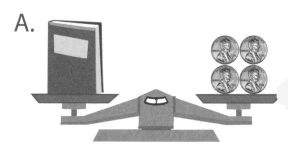

B.
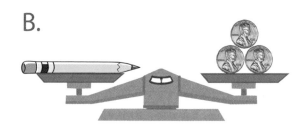

C.
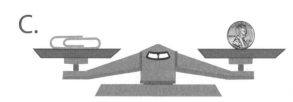

13. What is the shape of the faces on this figure?

A. circle

B. triangle

C. square

D. rectangle

14. What picture shows an oval?

A.

B. /

C. ◯

D. ▢

15. Look at the bar graph. Which student collected the fewest cans?

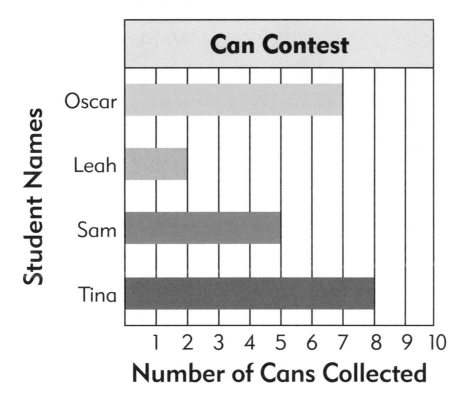

A. Oscar   B. Leah   C. Sam   D. Tina

16. Tom made a picture graph showing the number of bike rides he took each week

Which week did he take the most rides?

Bike Rides									
Week 1	🚲	🚲	🚲						
Week 2	🚲	🚲	🚲	🚲	🚲	🚲			
Week 3	🚲	🚲	🚲	🚲					
Week 4	🚲	🚲	🚲	🚲	🚲	🚲	🚲		

Each picture in the box equals 1.

A. Week 1   B. Week 2

C. Week 3   D. Week 4

17. Larry had some peanuts. He gave 14 peanuts to friends and now he has 15 peanuts left.

How many peanuts did Larry have in the beginning?

A. 1   B. 15

C. 29   D. 39

18. Which number sentence correctly solves this story problem?

Walter had some money. He gave away $21 to his sister and now Walter has $34 left.

How much money did Walter have in the beginning?

A. $34 - 21 = ?$

B. $21 - 34 = ?$

C. $34 + 21 = ?$

19. Keisha's paper chain has 45 links. If she takes 12 links off, Keisha's chain will have the same number of links as Mia's chain.

How many links are on Mia's paper chain?

A. 12

B. 33

C. 45

D. 57

20. Which best explains how to correctly solve this problem?

Peter picked 27 apples and Anna picked 12 apples. How many more apples did Peter pick than Anna?

    A. 12 − 27 because Anna picked more apples than Peter.

    B. 27 − 12 because Peter picked more apples than Anna.

    C. 27 + 12 because Peter picked more apples than Anna.

21. Which best explains how to correctly solve this problem?

Jonas has a coin collection. He had 24 quarters in his collection. He just added 6 new quarters.

How many quarters does Jonas have in his collection now?

    A. 24 − 6 because Jonas now has 6 fewer quarters than when he started.

    B. 24 − 6 because Jonas now has 6 more quarters than when he started.

    C. 24 + 6 because Jonas now has 6 more quarters than when he started.

22. John drew a picture to show his balloons. He had the fewest of which color balloon?

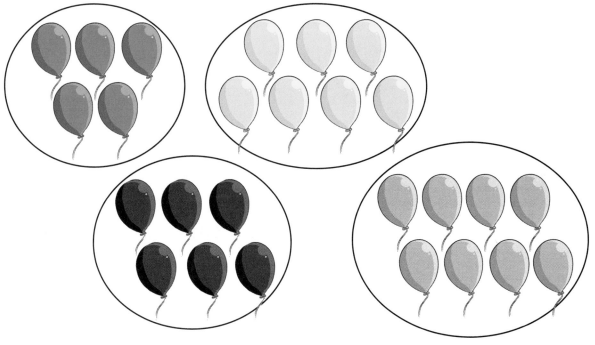

A. red

B. yellow

C. black

D. purple

23.   87
       + 4

A. 91   B. 90   C. 83   D. 81

Solve.

24.   48
       − 9

Addition Facts Chart

▶ Activity Objectives

- Demonstrate automatic recall of addition facts with sums through 8.
- Demonstrate automatic recall of addition facts with sums through 12.
- Demonstrate automatic recall of addition facts with sums through 16.
- Demonstrate automatic recall of addition facts with sums through 20.

Materials to Gather

ALSO NEEDED

poster board – 2 sheets, standard size (22 in. by 28 in.)

sticky notes – 22 of one color, 122 of another color – small, rectangular

meterstick or yardstick

tape

▶ Introduction

The Addition Facts Chart will help students keep track of the addition facts they know and the ones they still need to learn. Students will write a sum on a sticky note and place it on the correct place on the chart.

▶ Instruction

Set up the Addition Facts Chart on poster board.

1. Using the 22 sticky notes of one color, make two sets of numbers, one set from 0 to 10 with the long side of the sticky note along the bottom and another set from 0 to 10, also with the long side of the sticky note along the bottom. Write one number on each sticky note.

2. Write a plus sign on a sticky note of the other color and put it in the bottom left corner of the poster board.

3. Place one set of numbers (0 to 10) along the bottom of the chart. Place the other set of numbers (0 to 10) along the left-hand side of the chart.

4. Use a meterstick or yardstick to draw the two lines bordering the sticky notes. You can draw the interior grid lines, although the sticky notes to be placed within the grid will create the "boxes" shown. (Note: You may need to tape two standard sheets of poster board together to accommodate the entire chart.)

Addition Facts Chart

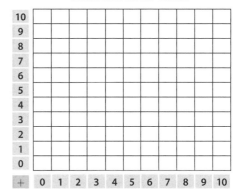

How to Use the Chart

Students will start with $0 + 0$ and will place sticky notes on the chart for all facts through $10 + 10$. For example, to place the sum of $3 + 1$, students will move horizontally from the plus sign on the chart to the column labeled 3 at the bottom of the chart and then up from there to the row labeled 1 along the side of the chart. Students will place the sum of $3 + 1$, or 4, in the box where the row and column meet. The sticky notes for the answers should be a different color from the 22 notes used to set up the chart.

Students should place a fact on the chart only when they have it memorized and can say it quickly. Otherwise, tell them they need more practice on that fact before they can place it on the chart.

Although this chart is not a coordinate graph, having the students first move horizontally, then vertically, lays the foundation for locating points on the coordinate graph.

Fact Groups

Students will complete the chart in stages, depending on how quickly they can learn the facts. Typically, students will learn the facts in the following stages:

- Addition facts with sums through 8
- Addition facts with sums through 12
- Addition facts with sums through 16
- Addition facts with sums through 20

As students progress through the facts, they will fill the chart as shown:

Sums Through 8

+	0	1	2	3	4	5	6	7	8	9	10
10											
9											
8	8										
7	7	8									
6	6	7	8								
5	5	6	7	8							
4	4	5	6	7	8						
3	3	4	5	6	7	8					
2	2	3	4	5	6	7	8				
1	1	2	3	4	5	6	7	8			
0	0	1	2	3	4	5	6	7	8		

Sums Through 12

+	0	1	2	3	4	5	6	7	8	9	10
10	10	11	12								
9	9	10	11	12							
8	8	9	10	11	12						
7	7	8	9	10	11	12					
6	6	7	8	9	10	11	12				
5	5	6	7	8	9	10	11	12			
4	4	5	6	7	8	9	10	11	12		
3	3	4	5	6	7	8	9	10	11	12	
2	2	3	4	5	6	7	8	9	10	11	12
1	1	2	3	4	5	6	7	8	9	10	11
0	0	1	2	3	4	5	6	7	8	9	10

Sums Through 16

+	0	1	2	3	4	5	6	7	8	9	10
10	10	11	12	13	14	15	16				
9	9	10	11	12	13	14	15	16			
8	8	9	10	11	12	13	14	15	16		
7	7	8	9	10	11	12	13	14	15	16	
6	6	7	8	9	10	11	12	13	14	15	16
5	5	6	7	8	9	10	11	12	13	14	15
4	4	5	6	7	8	9	10	11	12	13	14
3	3	4	5	6	7	8	9	10	11	12	13
2	2	3	4	5	6	7	8	9	10	11	12
1	1	2	3	4	5	6	7	8	9	10	11
0	0	1	2	3	4	5	6	7	8	9	10

Sums Through 20

+	0	1	2	3	4	5	6	7	8	9	10
10	10	11	12	13	14	15	16	17	18	19	20
9	9	10	11	12	13	14	15	16	17	18	19
8	8	9	10	11	12	13	14	15	16	17	18
7	7	8	9	10	11	12	13	14	15	16	17
6	6	7	8	9	10	11	12	13	14	15	16
5	5	6	7	8	9	10	11	12	13	14	15
4	4	5	6	7	8	9	10	11	12	13	14
3	3	4	5	6	7	8	9	10	11	12	13
2	2	3	4	5	6	7	8	9	10	11	12
1	1	2	3	4	5	6	7	8	9	10	11
0	0	1	2	3	4	5	6	7	8	9	10

When the Addition Facts Chart has been completed, students will know the following facts.

0 + 0 = 0	1 + 0 = 1	2 + 0 = 2	3 + 0 = 3	4 + 0 = 4	5 + 0 = 5
0 + 1 = 1	1 + 1 = 2	2 + 1 = 3	3 + 1 = 4	4 + 1 = 5	5 + 1 = 6
0 + 2 = 2	1 + 2 = 3	2 + 2 = 4	3 + 2 = 5	4 + 2 = 6	5 + 2 = 7
0 + 3 = 3	1 + 3 = 4	2 + 3 = 5	3 + 3 = 6	4 + 3 = 7	5 + 3 = 8
0 + 4 = 4	1 + 4 = 5	2 + 4 = 6	3 + 4 = 7	4 + 4 = 8	5 + 4 = 9
0 + 5 = 5	1 + 5 = 6	2 + 5 = 7	3 + 5 = 8	4 + 5 = 9	5 + 5 = 10
0 + 6 = 6	1 + 6 = 7	2 + 6 = 8	3 + 6 = 9	4 + 6 = 10	5 + 6 = 11
0 + 7 = 7	1 + 7 = 8	2 + 7 = 9	3 + 7 = 10	4 + 7 = 11	5 + 7 = 12
0 + 8 = 8	1 + 8 = 9	2 + 8 = 10	3 + 8 = 11	4 + 8 = 12	5 + 8 = 13
0 + 9 = 9	1 + 9 = 10	2 + 9 = 11	3 + 9 = 12	4 + 9 = 13	5 + 9 = 14
0 + 10 = 10	1 + 10 = 11	2 + 10 = 12	3 + 10 = 13	4 + 10 = 14	5 + 10 = 15

6 + 0 = 6	7 + 0 = 7	8 + 0 = 8	9 + 0 = 9	10 + 0 = 10
6 + 1 = 7	7 + 1 = 8	8 + 1 = 9	9 + 1 = 10	10 + 1 = 11
6 + 2 = 8	7 + 2 = 9	8 + 2 = 10	9 + 2 = 11	10 + 2 = 12
6 + 3 = 9	7 + 3 = 10	8 + 3 = 11	9 + 3 = 12	10 + 3 = 13
6 + 4 = 10	7 + 4 = 11	8 + 4 = 12	9 + 4 = 13	10 + 4 = 14
6 + 5 = 11	7 + 5 = 12	8 + 5 = 13	9 + 5 = 14	10 + 5 = 15
6 + 6 = 12	7 + 6 = 13	8 + 6 = 14	9 + 6 = 15	10 + 6 = 16
6 + 7 = 13	7 + 7 = 14	8 + 7 = 15	9 + 7 = 16	10 + 7 = 17
6 + 8 = 14	7 + 8 = 15	8 + 8 = 16	9 + 8 = 17	10 + 8 = 18
6 + 9 = 15	7 + 9 = 16	8 + 9 = 17	9 + 9 = 18	10 + 9 = 19
6 + 10 = 16	7 + 10 = 17	8 + 10 = 18	9 + 10 = 19	10 + 10 = 20

Horizontal Picture Graph

Each picture in the boxes equals 1.

Hundred Chart

1	2	3	4	5	6	7	8	9	10
11	12	13	14	15	16	17	18	19	20
21	22	23	24	25	26	27	28	29	30
31	32	33	34	35	36	37	38	39	40
41	42	43	44	45	46	47	48	49	50
51	52	53	54	55	56	57	58	59	60
61	62	63	64	65	66	67	68	69	70
71	72	73	74	75	76	77	78	79	80
81	82	83	84	85	86	87	88	89	90
91	92	93	94	95	96	97	98	99	100

Hundred Grid

Number Line 0–100

The number lines may be cut out and taped together to form a number line from 0 to 100.

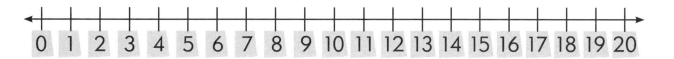

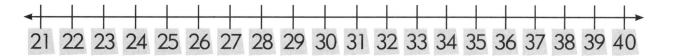

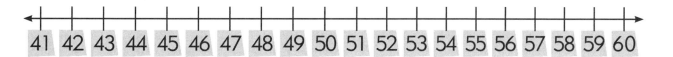

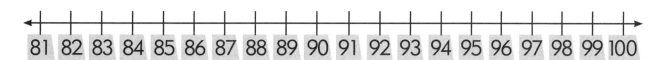

zero 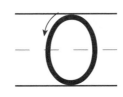 0 stars

one 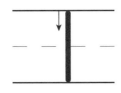 ☆
1 star

two  ☆ ☆
2 stars

three 3 ☆ ☆ ☆
3 stars

four 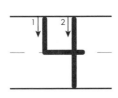 ☆ ☆
☆ ☆
4 stars

five

5

★ ★
☆ ☆ ☆
5 stars

six

6

☆ ☆ ☆
☆ ☆ ☆
6 stars

seven

7

☆ ☆ ☆
☆ ☆ ☆ ☆
7 stars

eight

8

☆ ☆ ☆ ☆
☆ ☆ ☆ ☆
8 stars

nine

9

☆ ☆ ☆
☆ ☆ ☆
☆ ☆ ☆
9 stars

Total

Part

Part

Start-Change-Result Chart

Some number sentences are written with the result shown first; other number sentences are written with the result shown last. Choose from the two different chart styles shown below depending on the number sentence presented in the Activity Book.

Start	+ or −	Change	=	Result

Start	+ or −	Change	=	Result

Result	=	Change	+ or −	Start

Result	=	Change	+ or −	Start

Subtraction Facts Chart

▶ Activity Objectives

- Demonstrate automatic recall of subtraction facts with minuends through 8.
- Demonstrate automatic recall of subtraction facts with minuends through 12.
- Demonstrate automatic recall of subtraction facts with minuends through 16.
- Demonstrate automatic recall of subtraction facts with minuends through 20.

Materials to Gather

ALSO NEEDED

poster board – 2 sheets – standard size (22 in. by 28 in.)

sticky notes – 32 of one color, 176 of another color – small, rectangular

meterstick or yardstick

tape

▶ Introduction

The Subtraction Facts Chart will help students keep track of the subtraction facts they know and the ones they still need to learn. Students will write a difference on a sticky note and place it on the correct place on the chart.

▶ Instructions

Set up the Subtraction Facts Chart on poster board.

1. You may start with one poster board or you may tape the poster boards together to get ready for the greater minuends. Using 32 sticky notes of one color, make two sets of numbers, one set from 0 to 20 with the long side of the sticky note along the bottom and another set from 0 to 10 also with the long side of the sticky note along the bottom. Write one number on each sticky note.

2. Write a minus sign on a sticky note of the other color and put it in the bottom left corner of the poster board.

3. Place the numbers 0 to 20 along the left-hand side of the chart. Those are the minuends. Place the numbers 0 to10 along the bottom of the chart. Those are the subtrahends.

4. Use a meterstick or yardstick to draw the two lines bordering the sticky notes. You can draw the interior grid lines, although the sticky notes to be placed within the grid will create the "boxes" shown.

   The n's in this diagram indicate numbers less than 0, or negative numbers. Students will not be subtracting numbers that will result in a numbers less than zero. You may want to put n's on sticky notes and put them in areas where negative numbers would appear so students will not think they need to fill in those areas.

Subtraction Facts Chart

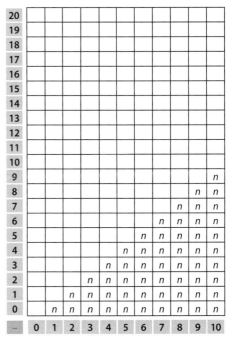

How to Use the Chart

Students will start with the answer to 0 − 0 and will place sticky notes on the chart for all the facts through 20 − 10. For example, to place the difference of 3 − 1, they will move up to row 3 and then over to the column labeled 1 on the bottom of the chart. Students will place the difference of 3 − 1, or 2, in the box where the column and row meet. The sticky notes for the answers should be a different color from the 32 notes used to set up the chart.

If the difference would be less than zero, or negative, such as 3 − 9, students should leave the box blank or leave the n you placed in the box.

Students should place a fact on the chart only when they have it memorized and can say it quickly. Otherwise, tell them they need more practice on that fact before they can place it on the chart.

On a similar chart for addition facts, students would have moved horizontally to locate the first addend and then vertically to find the second addend, just as they would in locating points on coordinate graphs. However, because subtraction is the inverse, or opposite, operation of addition, they will move in opposite directions on their subtraction charts— first vertically and then horizontally.

Fact Groups

Students will complete the chart in stages, depending on how quickly they can learn the facts. Typically, students will learn the facts in the following stages:

- Subtraction facts with minuends through 8
- Subtraction facts with minuends through 12
- Subtraction facts with minuends through 16
- Subtraction facts with minuends through 20

As students progress through the facts, they will fill the chart as shown:

Minuends Through 8

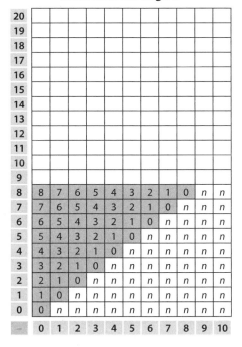

	0	1	2	3	4	5	6	7	8	9	10
20											
19											
18											
17											
16											
15											
14											
13											
12											
11											
10											
9											
8	8	7	6	5	4	3	2	1	0	n	n
7	7	6	5	4	3	2	1	0	n	n	n
6	6	5	4	3	2	1	0	n	n	n	n
5	5	4	3	2	1	0	n	n	n	n	n
4	4	3	2	1	0	n	n	n	n	n	n
3	3	2	1	0	n	n	n	n	n	n	n
2	2	1	0	n	n	n	n	n	n	n	n
1	1	0	n	n	n	n	n	n	n	n	n
0	0	n	n	n	n	n	n	n	n	n	n

Minuends Through 12

	0	1	2	3	4	5	6	7	8	9	10
20											
19											
18											
17											
16											
15											
14											
13											
12	12	11	10	9	8	7	6	5	4	3	2
11	11	10	9	8	7	6	5	4	3	2	1
10	10	9	8	7	6	5	4	3	2	1	0
9	9	8	7	6	5	4	3	2	1	0	n
8	8	7	6	5	4	3	2	1	0	n	n
7	7	6	5	4	3	2	1	0	n	n	n
6	6	5	4	3	2	1	0	n	n	n	n
5	5	4	3	2	1	0	n	n	n	n	n
4	4	3	2	1	0	n	n	n	n	n	n
3	3	2	1	0	n	n	n	n	n	n	n
2	2	1	0	n	n	n	n	n	n	n	n
1	1	0	n	n	n	n	n	n	n	n	n
0	0	n	n	n	n	n	n	n	n	n	n

Minuends Through 16

−	0	1	2	3	4	5	6	7	8	9	10
20											
19											
18											
17											
16	16	15	14	13	12	11	10	9	8	7	6
15	15	14	13	12	11	10	9	8	7	6	5
14	14	13	12	11	10	9	8	7	6	5	4
13	13	12	11	10	9	8	7	6	5	4	3
12	12	11	10	9	8	7	6	5	4	3	2
11	11	10	9	8	7	6	5	4	3	2	1
10	10	9	8	7	6	5	4	3	2	1	0
9	9	8	7	6	5	4	3	2	1	0	n
8	8	7	6	5	4	3	2	1	0	n	n
7	7	6	5	4	3	2	1	0	n	n	n
6	6	5	4	3	2	1	0	n	n	n	n
5	5	4	3	2	1	0	n	n	n	n	n
4	4	3	2	1	0	n	n	n	n	n	n
3	3	2	1	0	n	n	n	n	n	n	n
2	2	1	0	n	n	n	n	n	n	n	n
1	1	0	n	n	n	n	n	n	n	n	n
0	0	n	n	n	n	n	n	n	n	n	n

Minuends Through 20

−	0	1	2	3	4	5	6	7	8	9	10
20	20	19	18	17	16	15	14	13	12	11	10
19	19	18	17	16	15	14	13	12	11	10	9
18	18	17	16	15	14	13	12	11	10	9	8
17	17	16	15	14	13	12	11	10	9	8	7
16	16	15	14	13	12	11	10	9	8	7	6
15	15	14	13	12	11	10	9	8	7	6	5
14	14	13	12	11	10	9	8	7	6	5	4
13	13	12	11	10	9	8	7	6	5	4	3
12	12	11	10	9	8	7	6	5	4	3	2
11	11	10	9	8	7	6	5	4	3	2	1
10	10	9	8	7	6	5	4	3	2	1	0
9	9	8	7	6	5	4	3	2	1	0	n
8	8	7	6	5	4	3	2	1	0	n	n
7	7	6	5	4	3	2	1	0	n	n	n
6	6	5	4	3	2	1	0	n	n	n	n
5	5	4	3	2	1	0	n	n	n	n	n
4	4	3	2	1	0	n	n	n	n	n	n
3	3	2	1	0	n	n	n	n	n	n	n
2	2	1	0	n	n	n	n	n	n	n	n
1	1	0	n	n	n	n	n	n	n	n	n
0	0	n	n	n	n	n	n	n	n	n	n

When the Subtraction Facts Chart has been completed, students will know the following facts.

n	n	n	n	n	n	n	n	n	n
n	n	n	n	n	n	n	n	n	$9-9=0$
n	n	n	n	n	n	n	n	$8-8=0$	$9-8=1$
n	n	n	n	n	n	n	$7-7=0$	$8-7=1$	$9-7=2$
n	n	n	n	n	n	$6-6=0$	$7-6=1$	$8-6=2$	$9-6=3$
n	n	n	n	n	$5-5=0$	$6-5=1$	$7-5=2$	$8-5=3$	$9-5=4$
n	n	n	n	$4-4=0$	$5-4=1$	$6-4=2$	$7-4=3$	$8-4=4$	$9-4=5$
n	n	n	$3-3=0$	$4-3=1$	$5-3=2$	$6-3=3$	$7-3=4$	$8-3=5$	$9-3=6$
n	n	$2-2=0$	$3-2=1$	$4-2=2$	$5-2=3$	$6-2=4$	$7-2=5$	$8-2=6$	$9-2=7$
n	$1-1=0$	$2-1=1$	$3-1=2$	$4-1=3$	$5-1=4$	$6-1=5$	$7-1=6$	$8-1=7$	$9-1=8$
$0-0=0$	$1-0=1$	$2-0=2$	$3-0=3$	$4-0=4$	$5-0=5$	$6-0=6$	$7-0=7$	$8-0=8$	$9-0=9$

$10-10=0$	$11-10=1$	$12-10=2$	$13-10=3$	$14-10=4$	$15-10=5$	$16-10=6$	$17-10=7$	$18-10=8$	$19-10=9$	$20-10=10$
$10-9=1$	$11-9=2$	$12-9=3$	$13-9=4$	$14-9=5$	$15-9=6$	$16-9=7$	$17-9=8$	$18-9=9$	$19-9=10$	$20-9=11$
$10-8=2$	$11-8=3$	$12-8=4$	$13-8=5$	$14-8=6$	$15-8=7$	$16-8=8$	$17-8=9$	$18-8=10$	$19-8=11$	$20-8=12$
$10-7=3$	$11-7=4$	$12-7=5$	$13-7=6$	$14-7=7$	$15-7=8$	$16-7=9$	$17-7=10$	$18-7=11$	$19-7=12$	$20-7=13$
$10-6=4$	$11-6=5$	$12-6=6$	$13-6=7$	$14-6=8$	$15-6=9$	$16-6=10$	$17-6=11$	$18-6=12$	$19-6=13$	$20-6=14$
$10-5=5$	$11-5=6$	$12-5=7$	$13-5=8$	$14-5=9$	$15-5=10$	$16-5=11$	$17-5=12$	$18-5=13$	$19-5=14$	$20-5=15$
$10-4=6$	$11-4=7$	$12-4=8$	$13-4=9$	$14-4=10$	$15-4=11$	$16-4=12$	$17-4=13$	$18-4=14$	$19-4=15$	$20-4=16$
$10-3=7$	$11-3=8$	$12-3=9$	$13-3=10$	$14-3=11$	$15-3=12$	$16-3=13$	$17-3=14$	$18-3=15$	$19-3=16$	$20-3=17$
$10-2=8$	$11-2=9$	$12-2=10$	$13-2=11$	$14-2=12$	$15-2=13$	$16-2=14$	$17-2=15$	$18-2=16$	$19-2=17$	$20-2=18$
$10-1=9$	$11-1=10$	$12-1=11$	$13-1=12$	$14-1=13$	$15-1=14$	$16-1=15$	$17-1=16$	$18-1=17$	$19-1=18$	$20-1=19$
$10-0=10$	$11-0=11$	$12-0=12$	$13-0=13$	$14-0=14$	$15-0=15$	$16-0=16$	$17-0=17$	$18-0=18$	$19-0=19$	$20-0=20$

Subtraction Strategy Cards

Cut out the six cards and use them to review different strategies for subtraction.

Count Back	Memorize the Fact
12 − 2 = ? Start at 12 and count back 2. You may use the number line to count back. Say or think, "11, 10." 12 − 2 = 10	**12 − 2 = ?** Have you memorized the fact?
Use Blocks	Use a Related Addition Fact
12 − 2 = ? Start with 12 blocks. Take away 2 blocks. Count how many are left. Ten blocks are left. 12 − 2 = 10	**12 − 2 = ?** Think of a related addition fact. What number plus 2 equals 12? 10 plus 2 equals 12. So 12 − 2 = 10.
Use Other Subtraction Facts	Make Pairs
12 − 2 = ? Use a fact you know to find 12 − 2. A fact could be 10 − 2 = 8. Think, "12 is 2 more than 10." Because 2 more than 8 is 10, 12 − 2 = 10.	**12 − 2 = ?** Make pairs with circles. Count circles that are not paired. Ten circles are not paired. 12 − 2 = 10

